Macmillan McGraw-Hill

Math Connects 5

Chapter 1
Resource Masters

Macmillan/McGraw-Hill

The McGraw·Hill Companies

Macmillan/McGraw-Hill

Send all inquiries to:
Macmillan/McGraw-Hill
8787 Orion Place
Columbus, OH 43240-4027

ISBN: 978-0-02-107272-9
MHID: 0-02-107272-8

Printed in the United States of America.

6 7 8 9 10 DOD 16 15 14 13 12 11

Chapter 1 Resource Masters

Grade 5 Chapter 1
Table of Contents

Teacher's Guide to Using the *Chapter 1 Resource Masters*

The *Chapter 1 Resource Masters* includes the core materials needed for Chapter 1. These materials include worksheets, extensions, and assessment options. The answers for these pages appear at the back of this booklet.

All of the materials found in this booklet are included for viewing and printing on the *TeacherWorks Plus*™ CD-ROM.

Chapter Resources

Graphic Organizer (page 1) This master is a tool designed to assist students with comprehension of grade-level concepts. While the content and layout of these tools vary, their goal is to assist students by providing a visual representation from which they can learn new concepts.

Student Glossary (page 2) This master is a study tool that presents the key vocabulary terms from the chapter. You may suggest that students highlight or star the terms they do not understand. Give this list to students before beginning Lesson 1–1. Remind them to add these pages to their mathematics study notebooks.

Anticipation Guide (page 6) This master is a survey designed for use before beginning the chapter. You can use this survey to highlight what students may or may not know about the concepts in the chapter. There is space for recording how well students answer the questions before they complete the chapter. You may find it helpful to interview students a second time, after completing the chapter, to determine their progress.

Game (page 7) A game is provided to reinforce chapter concepts and may be used at appropriate times throughout the chapter.

Resources for Computational Lessons

Reteach Each lesson has an associated Reteach worksheet. In general, the Reteach worksheet focuses on the same lesson content but uses a different approach, learning style, or modality than that used in the Student Edition. The Reteach worksheet closes with computational practice of the concept.

Skills Practice The Skills Practice worksheet for each lesson focuses on the computational aspect of the lesson. The Skills Practice worksheet may be helpful in providing additional practice of the skill taught in the lesson.

Homework Practice The Homework Practice worksheet provides an opportunity for additional computational practice. The Homework Practice worksheet includes word problems that address the skill taught in the lesson.

Problem-Solving Practice The Problem-Solving Practice worksheet presents additional reinforcement in solving word problems that apply both the concepts of the lesson and some review concepts.

Enrich The Enrich worksheet presents activities that extend the concepts of the lesson. Some Enrich materials are designed to widen students' perspectives on the mathematics they are learning. These worksheets are written for use with all levels of students.

Resources for Problem-Solving Strategy and Problem-Solving Investigation Lessons In recognition of the importance of problem-solving strategies, worksheets for problem-solving lessons follow a slightly different format. For problem-solving lessons, a two-page Reteach worksheet offers a complete model for choosing a problem-solving strategy. For each Problem-Solving Strategy lesson, Reteach and Homework Practice worksheets offer reinforcement of the strategy taught in the Student Edition lesson. In contrast, the Problem-Solving Investigation worksheets include a model strategy on the Reteach worksheets and provide problems requiring several alternate strategies on the Homework Practice and Skills Practice worksheets.

Assessment Options The assessment masters in the *Chapter 1 Resource Masters* offer a wide variety of assessment tools for monitoring progress as well as final assessment.

Inventory Placement Test This two-page test covers key concepts from the previous year and tests what students are expected to bring to the current grade level.

Individual Progress Checklist This checklist explains the chapter's goals or objectives. Teachers can record whether a student's mastery of each objective is beginning (B), developing (D), or mastered (M). The checklist includes space to record notes to parents as well as other pertinent observations.

Chapter Diagnostic Test This one-page test assesses students' grasp of skills that are needed for success in the chapter.

Chapter Pretest This one-page quick check of the chapter's concepts is useful for determining pacing. Performance on the pretest can help you determine which concepts can be covered quickly and which specific concepts may need additional time.

Quizzes Three free-response quizzes offer quick assessment opportunities at appropriate intervals in the chapter.

Mid-Chapter Test This one-page chapter test provides an option to assess the first half of the chapter. It includes both multiple-choice and free-response questions.

Vocabulary Test This one-page test focuses on chapter vocabulary. It is suitable for all students. It includes a list of vocabulary words and questions to assess students' knowledge of the words.

Oral Assessment Although this two-page test assessment is designed to be used with all students, the interview format focuses on assessing chapter content assimilated by ELL students.

Chapter Project Rubric This one-page rubric is designed for use in assessing the chapter project. You may want to distribute copies of the rubric when you assign the project and use the rubric to record each student's chapter project score.

Foldables Rubric This one-page rubric is designed to assess the Foldables graphic organizer. The rubric is written to the students, telling them what you will be looking for as you evaluate their completed Foldables graphic organizer.

Leveled Chapter Tests

- **Form 1** assesses basic chapter concepts through multiple-choice questions and is designed for use with on-level students.

- **Form 2A** is designed for on-level students and is primarily for those who may have missed the Form 1 test. It may be used as a retest for students who received additional instruction following the Form 1 test.

- **Form 2B** is designed for students with a below-level command of the English language.

- **Form 2C** is a free-response test designed for on-level students.

- **Form 2D** is written for students with a below-level command of the English language.

- **Form 3** is a free-response test written for above-level students.

- ***Extended-Response Test*** is an extended response test for on-level students.

Cumulative Standardized Test Practice This three-page test, aimed at on-level students, offers three multiple-choice questions and free-response questions.

Student Recording Sheet This one-page recording sheet is for the standardized test in the Student Edition.

Answers

The answers for the Anticipation Guide and Lesson Resources are provided as reduced pages with answers appearing in black. Full size line-up answer keys are provided for the Assessment Masters.

Name _____ Date _____

Graphic Organizer

Use this graphic organizer to take notes on **Chapter 1: Use Place Value**.
Fill in the missing information.

Type of Number	Definition	Examples
Word Form		
Standard Form		
Expanded Form		

Name _____ Date _____

Student-Built Glossary

This is an alphabetical list of new vocabulary terms you will learn in **Chapter 1: Use Place Value**. As you study the chapter, complete each term's definition or description. Remember to add the page number where you found the term. Add this page to your math study notebook to review vocabulary at the end of the chapter.

Vocabulary Term	Found on Page	Definition/Description/Example
decimal		
decimal point		
equivalent decimals		
expanded form		

Name _____ Date _____

Student-Built Glossary (continued)

Vocabulary Term	Found on Page	Definition/Description/Example
place value		
standard form		
whole number		

MATH at HOME

Dear Family,

Today my class started **Chapter 1: Use Place Value**. I will be learning to use place value to read, write, and compare whole numbers and decimals. I will be learning to solve problems using the guess-and-check strategy. Here are my vocabulary words and an activity we can do together.

Sincerely, _____

Key Vocabulary

Whole number: Any one of the numbers 0, 1, 2, 3 ... In greater numbers, each group of three digits is separated by commas and is called a **period**.

Place value: A system for writing numbers. In this system, the position of a digit determines its value.

Standard form: The usual or common way to write a number. Example: 223.

Expanded form: A way of writing a number as the sum of the *values* of its digits. Example: 200 + 20 + 3.

Decimal: A number that has a digit in the tenths place, hundredths place, or beyond.

Activity

On a piece of paper have each player write four lines that will be filled in to create the largest number possible. Each player takes turns rolling a number cube and placing the digit they rolled on any line they choose. Once a digit is placed on a line it may not be moved. Continue rolling until each line is filled with a digit. The person who created the largest number wins.

Books to Read

The Grapes of Math
by Greg Tang

Math Curse
by Scieszka & Smith

Can You Count to a GOOGOL?
by Robert Wells

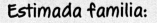

Estimada familia:

Hoy mi clase comenzó el **Capítulo 1, El valor de posición y el sentido numérico.** Aprenderé a usar el valor de posición para leer, escribir y comparar números enteros y decimales. Aprenderé a resolver problemas mediante la estrategia de adivinar y verificar. A continuación, están mis palabras del vocabulario y una actividad que podemos realizar juntos.

Sinceramente, _____

Vocabulario clave

número entero Cualquiera de los números 0, 1, 2, 3… En números más grandes, cada grupo de tres dígitos se separa con comas y se llama **período**.

valor de posición Sistema de escritura de números, en el cual la posición de un dígito determina su valor.

forma estándar La manera habitual de escribir un número. Ejemplo: 223.

forma desarrollada Manera de escribir un número como la suma de los *valores* de sus dígitos. Ejemplo 200 + 20 + 3.

decimal Número que tiene un dígito en el lugar de las decenas, centenas y más allá.

Activity

En un trozo de papel, cada jugador debe hacer cuatro líneas que se llenarán creando el número más grande posible. Cada jugador se turna para lanzar un cubo numerado y escribe el número que salga, en cualquiera de las líneas que escoja. Una vez que se escribe un número en una línea, éste no se puede mover. Continúen lanzando el cubo numerado hasta que cada línea esté llena con un dígito. Gana la persona que forme el número más grande.

Libros recomendados

**The Grapes of Math
(Las uvas de las matemáticas)**
de Greg Tang

**Math Curse
(El maleficio de las matemáticas)**
de Scieszka & Smith

**Can You Count to a GOOGOL?
(¿Puedes contar hasta un gúgol?)**
de Robert Wells

Name _____ Date _____

Anticipation Guide

Place Value and Number Sense

STEP 1 *Before you begin Chapter 1*

• Read each statement.

• Decide whether you agree (A) or disagree (D) with the statement.

• Write A or D in the first column OR if you are not sure whether you agree or disagree, write NS (Not Sure).

STEP 1 A, D, or NS	Statement	STEP 2 A or D
	1. The value of the 7 in the number 3,731,002 is 70,000	
	2. 5,692,001 > 5,692,000	
	3. The standard form of 39 thousand, 15 is 3,915	
	4. $\frac{87}{1,000} = 0.087$	
	5. The value of the 7 in the number 0.017 is 0.007	
	6. 0.990 = 0.99	

STEP 2 *After you complete Chapter 1*

• Reread each statement and complete the last column by entering an A (agree) or a D (disagree).

• Did any of your opinions about the statements change from the first column?

• For those statements that you mark with a D, use a separate sheet of paper to explain why you disagree. Use examples, if possible.

1

Game

What's Your Place?

Ready

You will need:

- A deck of cards
- 9 index cards

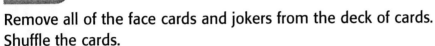
thousands

Set

Remove all of the face cards and jokers from the deck of cards.
Shuffle the cards.
Write the following on the index cards, one place value on each card:

ones	tens	hundreds
thousands	ten thousands	hundred thousands
millions	ten millions	hundred millions

Shuffle the index cards and place them face down on the table.

GO!

Object: Fill in the template with numbers that will create the answer you recorded on the answer line.

1. Deal each player 9 cards. Without looking at them, players line up their cards face down in a horizontal line.
2. Have players turn over their cards, one by one, to form a 9-digit number. Players may not change the order of their cards.
3. Choose an index card randomly and turn it over.
4. Compare the digits on the players' cards in the place value drawn.
5. Award each player the number of points of that digit.
6. Add up the scores. The player with the largest number after 10 rounds is the winner!

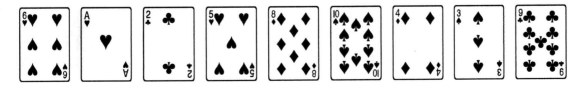

Chapter Resources

Reteach

Place Value Through Billions

A place-value chart can help you read greater numbers. Say the number in each period followed by the name of the period, except for the ones.

Billions Period			Millions Period			Thousands Period			Ones Period		
H	T	O	H	T	O	H	T	O	H	T	O
	4	7	3	0	2	0	1	6	2	9	4

Standard form: 47,302,016,294

Word form: 47 **billion**, 302 **million**, 16 **thousand**, 294
Read: forty-seven billion, three hundred two million, sixteen thousand, two hundred ninety-four

Expanded form: 40,000,000,000 + 7,000,000,000 + 300,000,000 + 2,000,000 + 10,000 + 6,000 + 200 + 90 + 4

Write the word form and the expanded form of each number. For help, complete the place-value chart.

1.

Billions Period			Millions Period			Thousands Period			Ones Period		
H	T	O	H	T	O	H	T	O	H	T	O

Standard form: 27,006,593

Word form: _____

Expanded form: _____

2. Standard form: 6,020,700,510

Word form: _____

Expanded form: _____

Name _____ Date _____

Skills Practice

Place Value Through Billions

Name the place value and write the value of the underlined digit.

1. 2,3<u>4</u>6 _____

2. 6<u>5</u>,893 _____

3. 7<u>6</u>3,406,594 _____

4. 40<u>7</u>,356,138,920 _____

5. 64,<u>3</u>21,008 _____

6. 1<u>1</u>7,927,724,417 _____

7. 903,00<u>4</u>,200,006 _____

Write each number in standard form.

8. 3 thousand, 125 _____

9. 52 thousand, 40 _____

Write each number in expanded form.

10. 7,450,693 _____

11. 531,017 _____

Write each number in word form.

12. 9,000,000,006 _____

13. 273,273 _____

Solve.

14. Mercury is the planet closest to the Sun. It orbits the Sun from a distance of about 28 million, 600 thousand miles. Write the number in standard form.

15. Neptune is the planet farthest from the Sun. It orbits the Sun from a distance of about 4 billion, 497 million miles. Write the number in standard form.

_____

_____

Name _____ Date _____

Homework Practice

Place Value Through Billions

Name the place value and write the value of the underlined digit.

1. 24<u>6</u>,007,112

_____

_____

2. <u>7</u>12,409,625

_____

_____

3. <u>8</u>56,415

_____

_____

4. <u>1</u>9,003,017

_____

_____

Write each number in expanded form.

5. 23,618

_____

_____

6. 105,770,000

_____

_____

_____

7. 1,413,001,000

_____

_____

_____

8. 25,501,261

_____

_____

1-1

Problem-Solving Practice

Place Value Through Billions

Solve.

1. The Nile River is 4,184 miles long. Write this number in expanded form.

   _____

2. According to the 2000 census, 8 million, 8 thousand, 278 people live in New York City. Write this number in standard form.

   _____

3. The distance around Earth is 24,902 miles. How do you read this number?

   _____

   _____

4. The distance around the planet Jupiter is 1,413,068,600 feet. Name the place and write the value of the underlined digit.

   _____

   _____

5. The population of Yorktown is 35,878. The population of Burlington is 4,530 less than the population of Yorktown. What is the total population of the two towns?

   _____

6. The population of California in 2001 was one hundred thousand more than 34,401,130. What was the population of California?

   _____

Name _____ Date _____

Enrich

Place Value Through Billions

This puzzle is similar to a crossword puzzle. Instead of writing letters in the boxes, write one digit in each box to form numbers. Use the clues below.

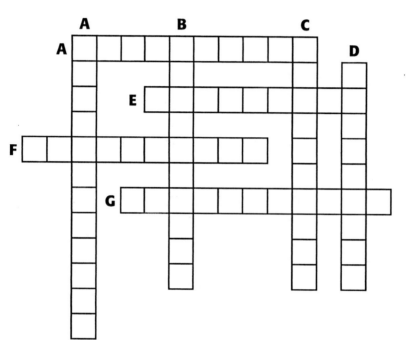

Across

A. the greatest possible number using each of the digits 0–9 once with a zero in the tens place

E. the least possible 9-digit number with a 2 in the hundred millions, hundred thousands, and hundreds places

F. 10 million more than 7 billion, 470 million, 100

G. 1 thousand more than 55 billion, 50 million, 5 thousand

Down

A. the greatest possible 12-digit number using an equal number of 6s, 7s, 8s, and 9s

B. the least possible 10-digit number using 5 as the first and last digit

C. the least possible number using each of the digits 0–9 once

D. 1 million more than 99 million

Look at the clue and number you wrote for B Down. Write two different clues for the same number.

_____

_____

Name _____ Date _____

Reteach

Compare Whole Numbers

You can write numbers in expanded form to compare them.

Compare 43,058 and 48,503.
Write the numbers in expanded form.

43,058 = 40,000 + 3,000 + 50 + 8
48,503 = 40,000 + 8,000 + 500 + 3

Compare the numbers, starting
with the greatest place.

40,000 = 40,000   3,000 < 8,000
So, 43,058 < 48,503.

**Write the numbers in expanded form. Replace each ◯ with
<, >, or = to make a true sentence.**

1. 3,505 = _____

3,055 = _____

3,505 ◯ 3,055

2. 432 = _____

4,322 =_____

432 ◯ 4,322

3. 8,296 = _____

596 = _____

8,296 ◯ 596

4. 5,324 = _____

9,736 = _____

5,324 ◯ 9,736

5. 4,000,976 = _____

4,009,076 = _____

4,000,976 ◯ 4,009,076

6. 1,104 = _____

1,140 = _____

1,104 ◯ 1,140

7. 9,076 = _____

1,942 = _____

9,076 ◯ 1,942

8. 4,103 = _____

4,130 = _____

4,103 ◯ 4,130

Name _____ Date _____

Skills Practice

Compare Whole Numbers

Replace each ◯ **with <, >, or = to make a true sentence.**

1. 1,040 ◯ 10

2. 14,092 ◯ 19,812

3. 840 ◯ 480

4. 1,001 ◯ 101

5. 123,778 ◯ 123,778

6. 9,879 ◯ 9,798

7. 6,823 ◯ 682

8. 5 ◯ 13

9. 190 ◯ 19

10. 71 ◯ 98

11. 192 ◯ 291

12. 611 ◯ 611

13. 314 ◯ 3,140

14. 657 ◯ 567

15. 324 ◯ 452

16. Michael ran 7 miles during one week. Krista ran 9 miles during one week. Who ran more miles?

_____

17. Jerry is 55 inches tall. Tom is 56 inches tall. Who is taller?

_____

Name _____ Date _____

Homework Practice

Compare Whole Numbers

Replace each ◯ with <, >, or = to make a true sentence.

1. 2,040 ◯ 20

2. 13,052 ◯ 16,912

3. 201 ◯ 2,001

4. 433,778 ◯ 433,778

5. 6,321 ◯ 282

6. 9 ◯ 13

7. 31 ◯ 38

8. 912 ◯ 921

9. 334 ◯ 3,340

10. 657 ◯ 567

Write the numbers in expanded form. Replace each ◯ with <, >, or = to make a true sentence.

11. 3,412 = _____

3,421 = _____

3,412 ◯ 3,421

12. 932 = _____

9,322 = _____

932 ◯ 9,322

Spiral Review

Write each number in standard form. (Lesson 1–1)

13. 11 million, 106 thousand, 300

_____

14. 91 billion, 13 million, 70 thousand, 2

_____

15. 300,000 + 20,000 + 300 + 70 + 8

_____

16. 1,000,000 + 50,000 + 9,000 + 4

_____

Name _____ Date _____

Problem-Solving Practice

Compare Whole Numbers

1. Kevin is 60 inches tall. His younger brother, Mike, is 62 inches tall. Who is taller?

_____

2. John Kennedy became president when he was 43 years old. George W. Bush became president when he was 54 years old. Who was older when he became president?

_____

3. There were about 22,859,968 people living in Texas in 2005. There were about 636,677 people living in North Dakota in 2005. Which state had fewer people in 2005?

_____

4. Texas has 254 counties. California has 58 counties. Which state has more counties?

_____

5. Texas became a state in 1845. South Carolina became a state in 1788. Which became a state later?

_____

6. The land area of Texas is 261,797 square miles. The land area of Alaska is 571,951 square miles. Which state has more land area?

_____

7. Texas has 115 state parks. Washington has 120 state parks. Which state has more state parks?

_____

8. Brewster can run one mile in 9 minutes. Alex can run one mile in 8 minutes. Who can run faster?

_____

Name _____ Date _____

Enrich

Compare and Order
Whole Numbers and Decimals

Each star below has a number next to it. Find the stars with a number greater than zero and less than 100 million. Connect the stars in order from least to greatest. Blast off!

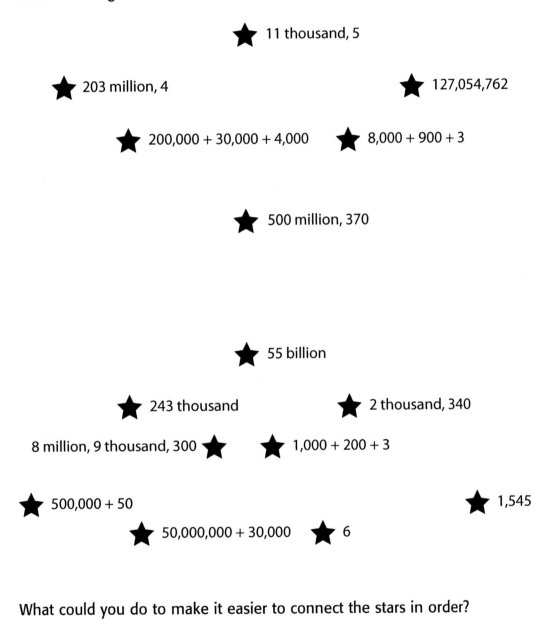

★ 11 thousand, 5

★ 203 million, 4   ★ 127,054,762

★ 200,000 + 30,000 + 4,000   ★ 8,000 + 900 + 3

★ 500 million, 370

★ 55 billion

★ 243 thousand   ★ 2 thousand, 340

8 million, 9 thousand, 300 ★   ★ 1,000 + 200 + 3

★ 500,000 + 50   ★ 1,545

★ 50,000,000 + 30,000   ★ 6

What could you do to make it easier to connect the stars in order?

_____

_____

Grade 5   **17**   Chapter 1

1-3

Reteach

Problem-Solving Investigation: Use the Four-Step Plan

The three tallest buildings in Boston are the Prudential Tower (750 ft), the John Hancock Tower (790 ft), and the Federal Reserve Building (604 ft). List these buildings from tallest to shortest.

Step 1 Understand	**Be sure you understand the problem.** Read carefully. Identify what you need to do. • What do you know? _____ • What have you been asked to do? _____
Step 2 Plan	You can compare the heights of the buildings. **Plan a strategy.** • Decide what actions you will take and in what order.
Step 3 Solve	**Solve the problem.** Follow your plan. Compare Prudential Tower and John Hancock Tower. $750 < 790$ Compare Prudential Tower and the Federal Reserve Building. $750 > 604$ The order from tallest to shortest is John Hancock Tower, Prudential Tower, Federal Reserve Building.
Step 4 Check	**Did you answer the question? Is the solution reasonable?** Yes, you have listed the buildings from tallest to shortest.

Solve. Use the four-step plan.

1. Scotia Plaza in Toronto is 902 feet tall. First Canadian Place in Toronto is 978 feet tall. Which building is taller?

_____

_____

2. Dallas' Renaissance Tower is 886 feet, Bank of America Plaza is 921 feet, and Bank One Center is 787 feet. List the buildings from shortest to tallest.

_____

_____

Name _____ Date _____

Reteach

Problem-Solving Investigation: Use the Four-Step Plan
(continued)

3. The Andersons are buying a paddle boat for $540. They plan to pay in four equal payments. How much will their payments be?

_____

4. Lynn can walk two miles in 24 minutes. At this rate, how long will it take her to walk 6 miles?

_____

5. Bridgit plays on the basketball team. The table shows the number of baskets she made in the first three days of practice. If the pattern continues, how many baskets will she make on Thursday and Friday?

Day	Baskets
Monday	21
Tuesday	22
Wednesday	24
Thursday	
Friday	

6. The Glendale Plaza Building in Glendale, California is 353 feet tall. The U.S. Bank Tower in Los Angeles, California is 1,017 feet tall. Which building is taller?

_____

7. After going on vacation, you come home with $5. You spent $6 on a pair of sunglasses, $10 on snacks, $4 on a book, and $5 on arcade games. How much money did you start with?

_____

Skills Practice

Problem-Solving Strategy: Use the Four-Step Plan

Solve. Use the four-step plan.

1. The three highest mountains in Colorado are Mount Massive (14,421 ft), Mount Harvard (14,420 ft), and Mount Elbert (14,433 ft). Which mountain has the greatest height?

_____

2. Hoover Dam, in the United States, is 223 meters high. Ertan Dam, in China, is 240 meters high. In Canada, Mica Dam is 243 meters high. List the dams by height from greatest to least.

_____

_____

3. The Akshi Kaikyo suspension bridge in Japan has a span of 6,570 feet. The Humber suspension bridge in England has a span of 4,626 feet. The Izmit Bay suspension bridge in Turkey has a span of 5,538 feet. Which bridge has the shortest span?

_____

4. There are three long tunnels that go under Boston Harbor. The Sumner Tunnel is 5,653 feet long. The Callahan Tunnel is 5,070 feet long. The Ted Williams Tunnel is 8,448 feet long. List the tunnels from shortest to longest.

_____

_____

5. List the tunnels in the table at the right by name in order from shortest to longest.

_____

_____

_____

Land Tunnels in the United States		
Tunnel	**State**	**Length (ft)**
Liberty Tubes	Pennsylvania	5,920
Devil's Side	California	3,400
E. Johnson Memorial	Colorado	8,959
Squirrel Hill	Pennsylvania	4,225

Name _____ Date _____

Homework Practice

Problem-Solving Investigation: Use the Four-Step Plan

Use the four-step plan to solve each problem.

1. A train left the station at 12:45. It traveled 455 miles in 7 hours. How many miles did it travel in each hour?

   _____

2. The Delgados are buying a pool that is 30 feet x 30 feet for $1,188. They plan to pay in 12 equal payments. Find the amount of each payment.

   _____

3. After shopping for school supplies, Martin came home with $4. He bought a pack of pens for $6, a calculator for $12, and a notebook for $3. How much money did he start with?

   _____

4. Julio increases the laps he runs by three laps each day. If he begins on Monday by running 4 laps, how many laps will he run on Wednesday at his current rate?

   _____

Spiral Review

Replace each ◯ with <, >, or = to make a true sentence. (Lesson 1–2)

5. 17 ◯ 8

   _____

6. 68 ◯ 93

   _____

7. 121 ◯ 1,210

   _____

8. 3,410 ◯ 3,401

   _____

9. 17,681 ◯ 16,681

   _____

10. 3,725,720 ◯ 3,752,720

   _____

Name _____ Date _____

Enrich

Summer Jobs

Solve. Use the four-step plan and the data from the table. You may use a calculator for exercises that require computation.

Earnings of Four Students During Summer Vacation				
Summer Job	Sabrina's Earnings	Tammi's Earnings	Ned's Earnings	Allen's Earnings
Babysitting	$620	$230	$140	$140
Gardening	$140	$20	$340	$260
Tutoring	$0	$440	$220	$0
Other	$90	$240	$160	$150

1. Which student earned the most money from tutoring?

_____

2. From what job did Ned earn the least money?

_____

3. Which student earned the most money from gardening?

_____

4. List Tammi's jobs from greatest earnings to least earnings.

_____

_____

5. Who earned more money in all, Sabrina or Tammi?

_____

6. List the students in order from the student with the least earnings to the student with the greatest earnings.

_____

_____

7. Write a problem that could be solved by comparing 3 or more numbers. Then give the problem to another student to solve.

_____

_____

Name _____ Date _____

Chapter Resources

Reteach

Represent Decimals

You can write a fraction as a decimal. Think of place value.

Fractions that name tenths, hundredths, and thousandths have one digit, two digits, and three digits to the right of the decimal point.

$\frac{1}{10}$	one tenth	0.1
$\frac{1}{100}$	one hundredth	0.01
$\frac{1}{1,000}$	one thousandth	0.001

Write each fraction as a decimal.

1. $\frac{65}{100}$ _____

2. $\frac{6}{10}$ _____

3. $\frac{86}{100}$ _____

4. $\frac{57}{100}$ _____

5. $\frac{5}{10}$ _____

6. $\frac{68}{100}$ _____

7. $\frac{25}{100}$ _____

8. $\frac{15}{100}$ _____

9. $\frac{4}{10}$ _____

10. $\frac{9}{10}$ _____

11. $\frac{2}{1,000}$ _____

12. $\frac{7}{10}$ _____

13. $\frac{11}{1,000}$ _____

14. $\frac{31}{100}$ _____

15. $\frac{19}{1,000}$ _____

16. $\frac{3}{1,000}$ _____

17. $\frac{3}{10}$ _____

18. $\frac{29}{1,000}$ _____

19. $\frac{4}{1,000}$ _____

20. $\frac{5}{1,000}$ _____

Name _____ Date _____

Skills Practice

Represent Decimals

Write each fraction as a decimal.

1. $\frac{3}{10}$ _____

2. $\frac{498}{1,000}$ _____

3. $\frac{7}{10}$ _____

4. $\frac{1}{10}$ _____

5. $\frac{947}{1,000}$ _____

6. $\frac{3}{10}$ _____

7. $\frac{18}{20}$ _____

8. $\frac{1}{50}$ _____

9. $\frac{11}{20}$ _____

10. $\frac{1}{10}$ _____

11. $\frac{256}{1,000}$ _____

12. $\frac{3}{100}$ _____

13. $\frac{77}{100}$ _____

14. $\frac{3}{100}$ _____

15. $\frac{13}{50}$ _____

16. $\frac{999}{1,000}$ _____

17. $\frac{9}{50}$ _____

18. $\frac{751}{1,000}$ _____

19. $\frac{7}{10}$ _____

20. $\frac{2}{10}$ _____

21. $\frac{1}{20}$ _____

22. $\frac{357}{1,000}$ _____

23. $\frac{1}{20}$ _____

24. $\frac{632}{1,000}$ _____

Solve.

25. The largest butterfly in the world is found in Papua, New Guinea. The female of the species weighs about 0.9 ounce. Use a fraction to write the female's weight.

_____

26. The shortest fish ever recorded is the dwarf goby found in the Indo-Pacific. The female of this species is about 0.35 inch long. Use a fraction to write the female's length.

_____

Name _____ Date _____

Homework Practice

Represent Decimals

Write each fraction as a decimal.

1. $\frac{3}{5}$ _____

2. $1\frac{1}{10}$ _____

3. $\frac{37}{50}$ _____

4. $\frac{29}{100}$ _____

5. $\frac{127}{200}$ _____

6. $\frac{1}{40}$ _____

7. $6\frac{3}{10}$ _____

8. $\frac{19}{20}$ _____

9. $9\frac{1}{20}$ _____

10. $8\frac{7}{10}$ _____

11. $2\frac{7}{20}$ _____

12. $\frac{477}{500}$ _____

13. $\frac{129}{200}$ _____

14. $\frac{391}{500}$ _____

15. $\frac{493}{1,000}$ _____

Spiral Review

Solve. Use the four-step plan. (Lesson 1–3)

16. There are 15 students going to the museum. If each student pays $7 for admission and $5 for lunch, what is the total cost for the 15 students?

_____

17. Meredith worked on her sewing project for 45 minutes every night for 4 nights. She worked on the project for 30 minutes a night for the rest of the week. How many minutes did she work on her project altogether?

_____

Name _____ Date _____

Problem-Solving Practice

Represent Decimals

Solve.

1. One cup is equal to 0.5 pint. Write this decimal as a fraction.

   _____

2. Aimee needs 0.25 cup of vegetable oil to make muffins. Write this decimal as a fraction.

   _____

3. Trudy is making a picture frame and needs nails that measure 0.375 of an inch. At the hardware store, nails are measured in fractions of an inch: $\frac{125}{1,000}$ inch, $\frac{25}{100}$ inch, and $\frac{375}{1,000}$ inch. Which of these nails should she buy?

   _____

4. At Richardson Elementary, 0.35 of the buses were late because of a snowstorm. Write the decimal as a fraction.

   _____

5. Neil needs several pieces of wood measuring $\frac{6}{10}$ foot each. The lumber store will cut pieces only in increments of 0.25 foot: 0.25 foot, 0.5 foot, 0.75 foot, and so on. Neil agrees to have the lumber store cut the pieces, but he will have to trim some off once he gets home. He wants to trim the least amount off each piece. Which measurement should the lumber store use to cut the pieces?

   _____

6. A vitamin contains sixty-two thousandths gram of vitamin E and 0.038 gram of vitamin A. Does the vitamin contain at least twice the amount of vitamin E than vitamin A?

   _____

7. Of the books at the Public Library, $\frac{25}{100}$ are for young readers. What decimal names this fraction?

   _____

8. Kathleen has recorded 0.4 of a book on to a cassette tape. What fraction of the book has she recorded?

   _____

Name _____ Date _____

Enrich

Grid Design

The grid area below is made up of 4 10-by-10 grids. Each 10-by-10 grid represents 1. Use three different color pencils or crayons to make a design on the grids. Color the grids completely.

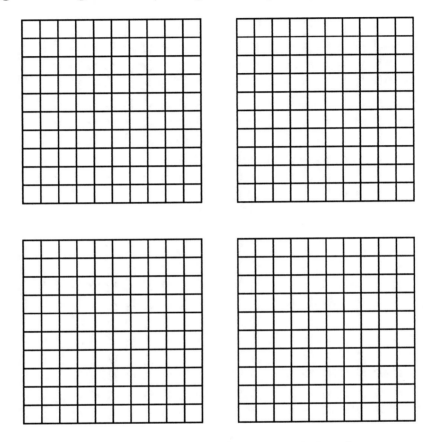

Write a decimal to tell what area you shaded with each color. Remember, 100 boxes (one grid) represent 1.

Color	Decimal

When was it necessary to write a decimal that included a whole number?

_____

_____

Name _____ Date _____

Reteach

Place Value Through Thousandths

The decimal 1.56 can be shown in several ways. The models below will show you different ways to represent 1.56.

You can use a place-value chart like the one below to represent 1.56.

1,000	100	10	1	0.1	0.01	0.001
Thousands	Hundreds	Tens	Ones	Tenths	Hundredths	Thousandths
0	0	0	1	5	6	

You can also represent 1.56 using a decimal model:

Represent the following decimals.

1. Use the place-value chart to show 0.87.

1,000	100	10	1	0.1	0.01	0.001
Thousands	Hundreds	Tens	Ones	Tenths	Hundredths	Thousandths

2. Use the decimal model to show 1.03.

Grade 5

Chapter 1

Name _____ Date _____

Skills Practice

Place Value Through Thousandths

Write the place value and the value of each underlined digit.

1. 2.<u>8</u> _____

2. 1.42<u>7</u> _____

3. 2.5<u>3</u>1 _____

4. 35.<u>0</u>52 _____

5. 5.3<u>5</u> _____

6. 24.00<u>2</u> _____

Write each number in standard form.

7. 5 and 34 thousandths _____

8. 34 and 12 hundredths _____

9. 20 + 4 + 0.7 + 0.04 + 0.005 _____

10. 100 + 7 + 0.05 + 0.007 _____

Write each number in expanded form and word form.

11. 23.5 _____

   _____

12. 164.38 _____

   _____

13. 4.292 _____

   _____

14. 53.007 _____

   _____

Name _____ Date _____

Homework Practice

Place Value Through Thousandths

Write the place value and the value of each underlined digit.

1. 2.65<u>4</u> _____ **2.** 1.8<u>2</u> _____

3. 3.8<u>7</u> _____ **4.** 4.<u>9</u>5 _____

5. 12.93<u>1</u> _____ **6.** 135.<u>4</u>82 _____

Write each number in standard form.

7. 17 and 134 thousandths _____

8. 263 and 4 hundredths _____

9. 10 + 0.04 + 0.002 _____

10. 4+ 0.9 + 0.01 + 0.006 _____

Write each number in expanded form.

11. 174.273 _____

12. 30.024 _____

13. 209.106 _____

14. 44.815 _____

Spiral Review

Write each fraction as a decimal. (Lesson 1–4)

15. $\frac{3}{10}$ _____ **16.** $\frac{1}{10}$ _____ **17.** $\frac{67}{100}$ _____

18. $\frac{7}{100}$ _____ **19.** $\frac{413}{1,000}$ _____ **20.** $\frac{5}{1,000}$ _____

Chapter Resources

1-5

Problem-Solving Practice

Place Value Through Thousandths

For Exercises 1–4, use the table.

The table shows lifetime batting averages for leading baseball players.

Lifetime Batting Averages for Leading Players		
Player	**Team**	**Batting Average**
Tony Gwynn, Jr.	Milwaukee Brewers	0.294
Derek Jeter	New York Yankees	0.341
Ichiro Suzuki	Seattle Mariners	0.319
Mike Piazza	San Diego Padres	0.277
Chipper Jones	Atlanta Braves	0.318

Source: mlb.com

1. Write Mike Piazza's batting average in word form.	**2.** Which digit is in the thousandths place of each player's batting average?
3. What is the batting average for the New York Yankees player in expanded form?	**4.** Which player's average has a 4 in the hundredths place?
5. When measuring board footage for some exotic woods, a carpenter must use 1.25 for thickness rather than 1 in her calculations. Write 1.25 in expanded form.	**6.** The summer camp Jason attends is exactly four hundred twenty-three and four tenths of a mile from his home. Write *four hundred twenty-three and four tenths* in standard form.

Name _____ Date _____

Enrich

Decimal Place Value

Part 1

Read each clue. Write the decimal, one digit on each answer line. Look carefully at the position of the decimal point. Circle the digit in the hundredths place.

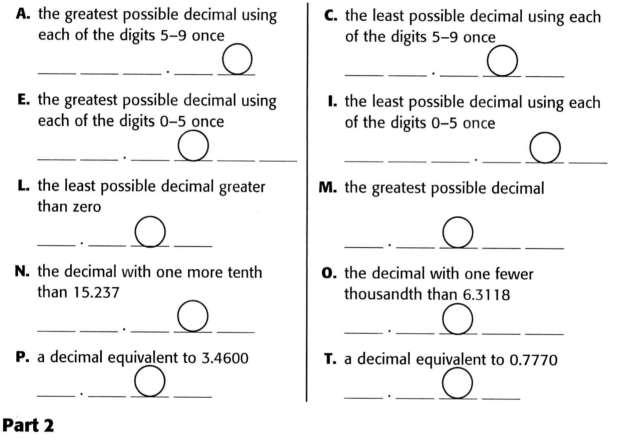

A. the greatest possible decimal using each of the digits 5–9 once

C. the least possible decimal using each of the digits 5–9 once

E. the greatest possible decimal using each of the digits 0–5 once

I. the least possible decimal using each of the digits 0–5 once

L. the least possible decimal greater than zero

M. the greatest possible decimal

N. the decimal with one more tenth than 15.237

O. the decimal with one fewer thousandth than 6.3118

P. a decimal equivalent to 3.4600

T. a decimal equivalent to 0.7770

Part 2

Use the problems above to solve a riddle. Match each digit you circled with one in the box below. Write the letter before the clue above the matching digit.

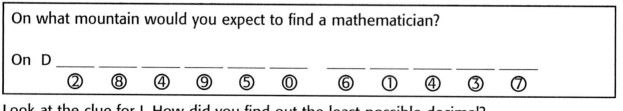

On what mountain would you expect to find a mathematician?

On D ____ ____ ____ ____ ____ ____   ____ ____ ____ ____ ____
       ②   ⑧   ④   ⑨   ⑤   ⓪   ⑥   ①   ④   ③   ⑦

Look at the clue for I. How did you find out the least possible decimal?

_____

_____

_____

1-6

Reteach

Compare Decimals

Compare 12.1 and 9.8.

Method 1

Use a number line.

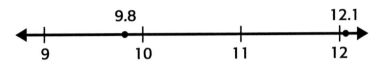

Numbers to the right are greater than numbers to the left.
Since 12.1 is to the right of 9.8, 12.1 > 9.8.

Method 2

Use place value.

Line up the decimal points.

If the numbers have a different number
of digits, be sure to line them up correctly.

12.1
 9.8

Only the number 12.1 has a digit in the tens place. So, 12.1 > 9.8.

Replace each ( ) with <, >, or = to make a true sentence.

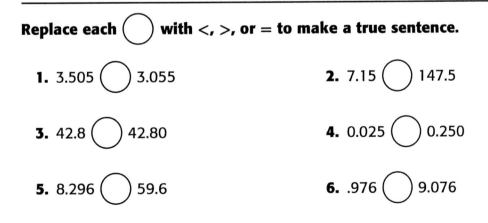

1. 3.505 ( ) 3.055

2. 7.15 ( ) 147.5

3. 42.8 ( ) 42.80

4. 0.025 ( ) 0.250

5. 8.296 ( ) 59.6

6. .976 ( ) 9.076

Name _____ Date _____

Skills Practice

Compare Decimals

Replace each ◯ with <, >, or = to make a true sentence.

1. 3.976 ◯ 4.007

2. 89.001 ◯ 89.100

3. 126.698 ◯ 126.689

4. 5.052 ◯ 5.052

5. 3.674 ◯ 6.764

6. 9.087 ◯ 9.807

7. 0.256 ◯ 0.256

8. 2.7 ◯ 2.82

9. 6.030 ◯ 6.03

10. 7.89 ◯ 7.189

11. 12.54 ◯ 1.254

12. 0.981 ◯ 2.3

13. 0.004 ◯ 0.040

14. 8.26 ◯ 8.6

15. 5.085 ◯ 5.805

16. 0.86 ◯ 0.168

17. 5.309 ◯ 5.003

Solve.

18. In January, the average low temperature in Montreal, Quebec, Canada, is 5.2°F, and the average low temperature in Cape Town, South Africa, is 60.3°F. Which city is warmer in January?

19. In one year Seattle, Washington, recorded 0.24 inch of snow, and Chicago, Illinois, recorded 30.9 inches of snow. Which city had more snow?

_____

_____

Name _____ Date _____

Homework Practice

Compare Decimals

Replace each ◯ with <, >, or = to make a true sentence.

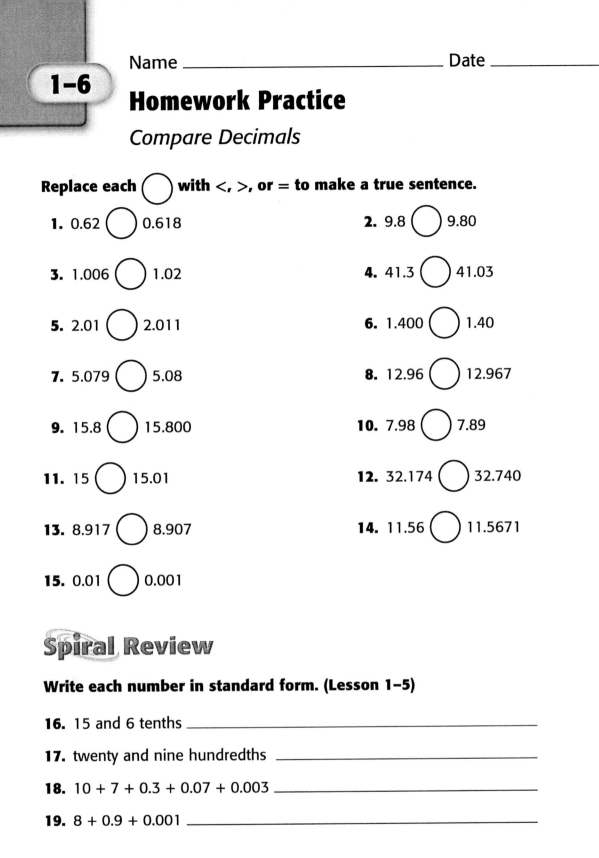

1. 0.62 ◯ 0.618

2. 9.8 ◯ 9.80

3. 1.006 ◯ 1.02

4. 41.3 ◯ 41.03

5. 2.01 ◯ 2.011

6. 1.400 ◯ 1.40

7. 5.079 ◯ 5.08

8. 12.96 ◯ 12.967

9. 15.8 ◯ 15.800

10. 7.98 ◯ 7.89

11. 15 ◯ 15.01

12. 32.174 ◯ 32.740

13. 8.917 ◯ 8.907

14. 11.56 ◯ 11.5671

15. 0.01 ◯ 0.001

Spiral Review

Write each number in standard form. (Lesson 1–5)

16. 15 and 6 tenths _____

17. twenty and nine hundredths _____

18. 10 + 7 + 0.3 + 0.07 + 0.003 _____

19. 8 + 0.9 + 0.001 _____

Name _____ Date _____

Problem-Solving Practice

Compare Decimals

Solve.

1. Two newborn babies are weighed at the hospital. The baby girl weighs 7.25 lb, and the baby boy weighs 7.3 lb. Which baby weighs more?

   _____

2. George was weighed at the doctor's office. The scale read 67.20 lb, but the doctor wrote 67.2 lb on George's chart. Did the doctor make a mistake?

   _____

3. Two of the highest mountains in the world are Nanga Parbat (Pakistan), and Dhaulagiri (Nepal). They measure 26,660 ft and 26,810 ft, respectively. Which of the two mountains is the lower?

   _____

4. Write all possible missing digits that make the sentence 49.76 > 49._6 true.

   _____

5. The two fastest times in a race were 9.789 seconds and 9.76 seconds. Which is the better time?

   _____

6. The two fastest times in the past 20 years for the girls' 200-meter run at Clarksville Elementary School are 27.97 seconds and 27.93 seconds. At yesterday's track meet, Claire ran 27.99 seconds. Was her time better than either of the two fastest?

   _____

7. Two divers have entered a competition. The scores are 9.75 and 9.79. What is the better score?

   _____

8. The times for the first two runners of the 100-yard dash are 9.85 seconds and 9.62 seconds. What is the winning time?

   _____

Name _____ Date _____

Enrich

Compare and Order

Rearrange the digits in each number in the given statement to make a new true statement.

Example: 3,427 < 3,825 **can become** 7,342 > 5,382
   or 2,734 > 2,385   **or** 2,347 < 5,823

1. 585 > 597 _____

2. 4,268 > 2,684 _____

3. 23,627 < 24,745 _____

4. 313,546 < 331,645 _____

Using all of the digits given, write a decimal number to make each statement true. Use each digit only once in each number.

Use 5, 6, 8, 9, and 0.

5. 0.8659 < _____ < 0.8956

6. 5.698 > _____ > 5.6809

7. 68.509 < _____ < 68.950

8. 8.6950 > _____ > 8.6095

Use 1, 2, 3, 4, and 0.

9. 0.2341 < _____ < 0.2431

10. 3.0124 < _____ < 3.1042

11. 4.1023 > _____ > 4.0132

12. 14.023 < _____ < 14.203

13. List your answers for exercises 5–12. Order the numbers from greatest to least.

_____

_____

37

Name _____ Date _____

Reteach

Order Whole Numbers and Decimals

You can write numbers in expanded form to compare them.

- Compare 43,058 and 48,503.
  Write the numbers in expanded form.

  $43,058 = 40,000 + 3,000 + 50 + 8$

  $48,503 = 40,000 + 8,000 + 500 + 3$

  Compare the numbers, starting
  with the greatest place.

  | $40,000 = 40,000$ | $3,000, < 8,000$ |

  So, $43,058, < 48,503$.

- Compare 12.106 and 9.837.
  If the numbers have a different number
  of digits, be sure to line them up correctly.

  $12.106 = 10 + 2 + 0.1 + \qquad 0.006$

  $9.837 = \qquad 9 + 0.8 + 0.03 + 0.007$

  Only the number 12.106 has a digit in
  the tens place. So, $12.106 > 9.837$.

Write the numbers in expanded form. Replace each $\bigcirc$ with $>$, $<$ or $=$ to compare each pair of numbers.

1. $3,505 =$ _____

$3,055 =$ _____

$3,505 \bigcirc 3,055$

2. $7.15 =$ _____

$17.5 =$ _____

$7.15 \bigcirc 17.5$

3. $42.8 =$ _____

$42.80 =$ _____

$42.8 \bigcirc 42.80$

4. $0.025 =$ _____

$0.250 =$ _____

$0.025 \bigcirc 0.250$

5. $8,296 =$ _____

$596 =$ _____

$8,296 \bigcirc 596$

6. $4,000,976 =$ _____

$4,009,076 =$ _____

$4,000,976 \bigcirc 4,009,076$

Name _____ Date _____

Skills Practice

Order Whole Numbers and Decimals

Replace each ◯ **with >, <, or = to compare each pair of numbers.**

1. 3,976 ◯ 4,007

2. 89,001 ◯ 89,100

3. 126,698 ◯ 126,689

4. 1,435,052 ◯ 145,052

5. 19,463,674 ◯ 29,436,764

6. 4,303,259,087 ◯ 4,033,259,807

7. 2.7 ◯ 2.82

8. 6.030 ◯ 6.03

9. 7.89 ◯ 7.189

10. 12.54 ◯ 1.254

11. 0.981 ◯ 2.3

12. 0.004 ◯ 0.040

Order each set of numbers from *least* to *greatest*.

13. 17,639; 3,828; 45,947 _____

14. 890,409; 890,904; 809,904 _____

15. 0.186; 0.1; 0.86; 0.168 _____

16. 5.309; 5.003; 0.53; 0.9 _____

Solve.

17. In City A, the average low temperature is 7.4°F, and the average low temperature in City B is 54.1°F. Which city is warmer?

_____

18. In one year Seattle recorded 0.24 inch of snow, Chicago recorded 30.9 inches of snow, and Birmingham recorded 1 inch of snow. Write these amounts in order from least to greatest.

_____

Name _____ Date _____

Homework Practice

Order Whole Numbers and Decimals

Replace each 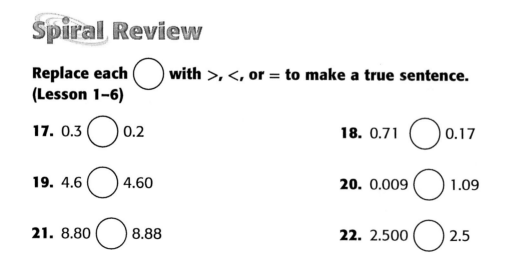 with >, <, or = to compare each pair of decimals.

1. 0.788 ⬤ 0.778 _____

2. 1.1 ⬤ 1.10 _____

3. 4.052 ⬤ 4.05 _____

4. 0.0549 ⬤ 0.549 _____

5. 4.563 ⬤ 0.4563 _____

6. 0.00783 ⬤ 0.00837 _____

7. 9.34132 ⬤ 9.31432 _____

8. 7.341 ⬤ 70.041 _____

9. 0.30 ⬤ 0.3000 _____

10. 1.8091 ⬤ 1.8901 _____

11. 8.34 ⬤ 8.43 _____

12. 0.23441 ⬤ 0.34421 _____

13. 0.0120 ⬤ 0.012 _____

14. 2.5038 ⬤ 2.3058 _____

Order each set of decimals from *least* to *greatest*.

15. 2.654, 2.564, 2.0564, 2.465 _____

16. 1.11, 0.111, 1.01, 1.0011 _____

Spiral Review

Replace each ( ) with >, <, or = to make a true sentence. (Lesson 1–6)

17. 0.3 ( ) 0.2

18. 0.71 ( ) 0.17

19. 4.6 ( ) 4.60

20. 0.009 ( ) 1.09

21. 8.80 ( ) 8.88

22. 2.500 ( ) 2.5

1–7

Problem-Solving Practice

Order Whole Numbers and Decimals

Solve.

1. The table shows the heights of four students. Arrange the students in order from shortest to tallest.

Student Heights	
Name	**Height (in.)**
Kim	56.03
Alexa	56.3
Roy	56.14
Tom	57.1

_____

2. Two boxes to be mailed are weighed at the post office. Box A weighs 8.25 pounds, and the box B weighs 8.2 pounds. Which box weighs more?

_____

3. Three airplanes flew from New York to Los Angeles. Fast Jet flew at an altitude of 38,500 feet. Sky High flew at 37,950 feet. Air Jet flew at 38,420 feet. Which jet flew at the lowest altitude?

_____

4. The four fastest times in a race were 27.08 seconds, 27.88 seconds, 27.8 seconds, and 26.78 seconds. Order these times from least to greatest.

_____

5. Misha's cat was weighed at the vet's office. The scale read 9.120 pounds, but the doctor wrote 9.12 pounds on the chart. Did the doctor make a mistake?

_____

6. Write all possible missing digits that make the sentence 51.38 > 51.☐8 true.

_____

7. The three fastest times in the past 20 years for the girls' 400-meter run at Clarksville Elementary School are 59.65 seconds, 59.76 seconds, and 61.02 seconds. At yesterday's track meet, Claire ran 59.93 seconds and Leslie ran 61.26 seconds. Should either girl's time be included in the list of top 3 times?

_____

8. Lauren spent $3.26 for lunch on Tuesday. She spent $1.98 on Wednesday and $2.74 on Thursday. Order the prices of her lunches from greatest to least.

_____

Enrich

Hurdling the Competition

Use the data from the table to solve.

Men's Olympic 400-Meter Hurdles		
Year	**Gold Medal Winner**	**Time (in seconds)**
1980	Volker Beck	48.70
1984	Edwin Moses	47.75
1988	Andre Phillips	47.19
1992	Kevin Young	46.78
1996	Derrick Adkins	47.54
2000	Angelo Taylor	47.50
2004	Felix Sanchez	47.63

1. List Andre Phillips, Kevin Young, and Derrick Adkins from fastest to slowest.

   _____

2. Which gold medal winner has the fastest time in the 400-meter hurdles?

   _____

3. How much less time did it take Angelo Taylor in 2000 than it took Derrick Adkins in 1996?

   _____

4. Which athlete has the slowest time?

   _____

5. In 1976, Edwin Moses won a gold medal in the 400-meter hurdles with a time of 47.64 seconds. How much faster was his time in 1976 than in 1984?

   _____

6. What are the athlete's names in order from slowest time to fastest time?

   _____

7. Who had a time 0.25 second faster than Edwin Moses had in 1984?

   _____

8. In what year did an athlete have a gold-medal-winning time of 0.19 second more than 47 seconds?

   _____

9. What is the difference between the fastest time and the slowest time?

   _____

10. How many years after Andre Phillips won a gold medal did Felix Sanchez win a gold medal?

   _____

Name _____ Date _____

Reteach

Problem-Solving Strategy: Guess and Check

Guess and Check

During summer vacation, Sanjay writes letters and postcards to his friends at home. A letter costs $0.41 to mail, and a postcard costs $0.21 to mail. Sanjay writes to 8 friends and spends $2.08. How many letters and postcards does he send?

Step 1
Understand
	Be sure you understand the problem.
	Read carefully. Identify what you need to do.
	What facts do you know?
	   • A letter costs _____ and a postcard costs _____
	     to mail.
	   • Sanjay writes to _____.
	   • He spends _____.
	What do you need to find?
	   • The number of _____.

Step 2 Plan • Use Logical Reasoning • Draw a Diagram • Make a Graph • Make a Table or List • Find a Pattern • Guess and Check	**Make a plan.** Choose a strategy. You can solve the problem by making a guess. Then check the guess. If it is not the correct answer, adjust the guess and check again until you find the correct answer.

Reteach

Problem-Solving Strategy: Guess and Check

Step 3 Solve	**Follow your plan.**
	Make a guess about the number of letters and the number of postcards. Suppose you guess 4 letters and 4 postcards.
	Check the amounts for the guess.
	Letters: _____ × _____ = _____
	Postcards: _____ × _____ = _____
	Total Cost: _____ + _____ = _____
	Does the guess check with the total that Sanjay spent? _____
	Should you adjust the number of letters up or down? Explain.
	_____
	_____
	Adjust your guess. Check your guess.
	Did the guess check? _____
	If your guess did not check, adjust it again.
	How many letters does Sanjay send? _____
	How many postcards does Sanjay send? _____
Step 4 Check	**Look back. Did you answer the question?** Is the solution reasonable? Reread the problem.
	Have you answered the question? _____
	How can you check your answer? _____
	_____

Practice

1. Nelson has 7 coins. All the coins are dimes and quarters. He has a total of $1.15. How many dimes and how many quarters does he have?

   _____

2. The library charges $0.75 a day for overdue videos and $0.12 a day for overdue books. Emily returns a video and a book and pays a total of $3.48 in late fees. How many days late were her items?

   _____

Name _____ Date _____

Skills Practice

Problem-Solving Strategy: Guess and Check

Use the guess and check strategy to solve.

1. The Bactrian camel has two humps and the Dromedary camel has one hump. In a group of 15 camels, the total number of humps is 21. How many camels of each type are there?

2. The circus orders bicycles and unicycles for a new act. It orders a total of 12 cycles. The cycles have 16 tires altogether. How many bicycles and unicycles did the circus order?

3. Anja buys a magazine and a pizza. She spends $8.10. The magazine costs $2.40 less than the pizza. How much does the pizza cost?

4. A letter to Europe from the United States costs $0.80 to mail. A letter mailed within the United States costs $0.41. Nancy mails 5 letters for $2.83, some to Europe and some to the United States. How many letters did she send to Europe?

5. Warren spent $8.50 at the store. He spent $2.40 on paper, $0.88 on pencils, and $2.65 on markers. He spent the rest on a notebook. How much did the notebook cost?

6. Ms. Baxter takes a group of 8 children to a concert. Tickets for children 12 years and older cost $3.50. Tickets for children under 12 cost $2.25. She spends a total of $21.75 on tickets for the children. How many children are 12 and older?

Name _____ Date _____

Homework Practice

Problem-Solving Strategy: Guess and Check

Use the *guess and check* strategy to solve.

1. Jamal is thinking of four numbers from 1 through 9 whose sum is 21. Find the numbers.

   _____

2. Mr. Thompson took his 5 children to the amusement park. Tickets for children 12 and older cost $3.50. Tickets for children under 12 cost $2.25. He spends a total of $16.25. How many of his children are 12 and older?

   _____

3. A cabin has room for 7 campers and 2 counselors. How many cabins are needed for a total of 49 campers and 14 counselors?

   _____

Spiral Review

Order each set of numbers from *least* to *greatest*. (Lesson 1–7)

4. 147, 111, 175, 121 _____

5. 19.1, 15.3, 13.7, 18.5 _____

6. 0.83, 0.32, 0.88, 0.23 _____

7. 11,525; 11,125; 11,725; 11,225 _____

Name _____ Date _____

Enrich

Benchmark Numbers

Use the benchmark number on the left to estimate the number in the picture on the right.

1.

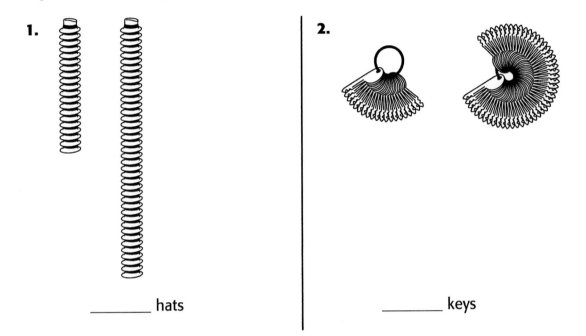

_____ hats

2.

_____ keys

Use the benchmark number to draw each item described.

3. The pickle barrel below holds 300 pickles. Draw a pickle barrel that could hold 900 pickles.

4. The necklace below has 50 beads. Draw a necklace that is long enough to hold 100 beads.

Name _____ Date _____

Inventory Placement Test

Read each question carefully. Fill in the correct answer in the space provided.

1. Order the numbers from greatest to least.
83,083, 38,803, 38,830, 83,308

1. _____

2. $310.75 + $28.09

2. _____

3. Complete the equation to make it balanced.
3 quarters + 1 dime + 7 pennies = 2 quarters +
2 pennies + ☐

3. _____

4. Write a rule as an equation to describe the pattern in the table.

Input (x)	Output (y)
5	3
10	8
15	13
20	18

4. _____

5. Look at the line graph below.
In what month were the most cones sold?

Ice Cream Cones Sold

5. _____

6. Jeremy's math test scores are listed below.
99, 81, 81, 99, 90, 99, 73
What is the mode of Jeremy's math test scores?

6. _____

7. What two composite numbers are greater than 22 and less than 26?

7. _____

8. Find the value of $4 + 3 \times t$ if $t = 3$.

8. _____

9. Benito gives 7 grapes to Ray. Then Benito eats 11 grapes. If Benito has 14 grapes left, how many grapes did he have originally?

9. _____

Name _____ Date _____

Inventory Placement Test (continued)

Assessment

10. Find the value of y if $709 \times 51 = y$.

11. $8\overline{)971}$

12. There are 103 students in fifth grade at Dane's school. The students are divided among 4 classes. About how many students are in each class?

13. A triangle has sides that each measure 3 centimeters. All three of its angles measure 60°. Identify the triangle as isosceles, equilateral, or scalene. Also identify it as acute, right, or obtuse.

14. A rectangular gymnasium has an area of 96 square feet and a width of 8 feet. What is the length of the gymnasium?

15. Look at the coordinate plane. What ordered pair names point A?

```
8               H
7        A
6  E
5            S
4      Y
3  W
2    V      R
1   O        N
   T
0  1 2 3 4 5 6 7 8
```

16. Find the value of x if $\dfrac{14}{35} = \dfrac{2}{x}$.

17. Write $4\dfrac{9}{6}$ as a mixed number.

18. Write $\dfrac{7}{100}$ as a decimal.

19. $59.07 - 19.8$

20. Lexi tosses 2 quarters. What is the probability that both coins will land on heads?

10. _____

11. _____

12. _____

13. _____

14. _____

15. _____

16. _____

17. _____

18. _____

19. _____

20. _____

Name _____ Date _____

Individual Progress Checklist

Learning Mastery			Lesson	Lesson Goal	Comments
B	**D**	**M**			
			1-1	Read and write whole numbers in standard form, expanded form, word form, and short word form.	
			1-2	Compare whole numbers	
			1-3	Use the four-step plan to solve a problem.	
			1-4	Represent fractions that name tenths, hundredths, and thousandths as decimals.	
			1-5	Read and write decimals in standard form, expanded form, and short word form.	
			1-6	Compare decimals.	
			1-7	Order whole numbers and decimals	
			1-8	Solve problems by using the *guess and check* strategy.	

B = Beginning; **D** = Developing; **M** = Mastered

Note to Parents

_____

_____

_____

_____

_____

_____

_____

_____

Chapter Diagnostic Test

Write each number in words.

1. 6 _____

2. 18 _____

3. 34 _____

4. 41 _____

5. 150 _____

6. 271 _____

Write the value of each point on the number line.

```
      A   B      C   D         E F
  ◄——+—+—+—+—+—+—+—+—+—+—+—+—+—+—+—+—►
     0  1  2  3  4  5  6  7  8  9 10 11 12 13 14 15 16
```

7. A _____

8. F _____

9. B _____

10. D _____

11. C _____

12. E _____

Write each sentence using the symbols <, >, or =.

13. 5 is less than 9 _____

14. 41 is greater than 12 _____

15. 92 is equal to 92 _____

16. 231 is greater than 230 _____

17. Sandy collected 16 seashells. Mark collected 14 seashells. Write *14 is less than 16* using symbols. _____

Name _____ Date _____

Chapter Pretest

Name the place value of the underlined digit.

1. 1,567,9<u>4</u>4

2. 13,4<u>89</u>,012

3. 699,<u>8</u>79

4. <u>4</u>01,555,223

1. _____

2. _____

3. _____

4. _____

Replace each □ with <, >, or = to make a true sentence.

5. 9 □ 13

6. 23,529 □ 23,528

7. 0.08 □ 0.080

8. 6.29 □ 6.33

5. _____

6. _____

7. _____

8. _____

Write each fraction as a decimal.

9. $\frac{683}{1,000}$

10. $\frac{7}{10}$

11. $\frac{6}{100}$

12. $\frac{91}{100}$

9. _____

10. _____

11. _____

12. _____

Name _____ Date _____

Quiz 1 *(Lessons 1–1 through 1–3)*

Write each number in standard form.

1. three million, nine hundred thirty-nine thousand, four hundred two

2. 13 million, 304 thousand, 12

3. 10,000 + 9,000 + 500 + 60

1. _____

2. _____

3. _____

Write each number in word form.

4. 2,897

5. 6,000,700,002

4. _____

5. _____

Replace each □ with <, >, or = to make a true sentence.

6. 13 □ 13

7. 73,529 □ 73,528

8. 927 □ 972

9. 1,290 □ 129

6. _____

7. _____

8. _____

9. _____

Use the four-step plan to solve each problem.

10. Chris has $85 to spend on a jacket. The jacket costs $40. If he buys one jacket, he gets the second for half price. How much money will he have left if he purchases two jackets?

11. Manny cut his pizza into 6 slices and ate 3 of them. Rachel cut her pizza into 8 slices and ate 5 of them. If the pizzas were the same size, who ate more?

10. _____

11. _____

Name _____ Date _____

Quiz 2 *(Lessons 1–4 through 1–6)*

Write each fraction as a decimal.

1. $\frac{3}{10}$

2. $\frac{673}{100}$

3. $\frac{9}{100}$

1. _____

2. _____

3. _____

Write the place value and the value of each underlined digit.

4. 3.<u>9</u>2

5. 4.10<u>2</u>

4. _____

5. _____

Write each number in standard form.

6. forty and nine hundredths

7. 7 + 0.01 + 0.008

6. _____

7. _____

Replace each □ with <, >, or = to make a true sentence.

8. 9 □ 10

9. 4,529 □ 4,528

10. 0.20 □ 0.200

8. _____

9. _____

10. _____

11. A town got 2.76 inches of rain during a rainstorm. Write this number in expanded form.

11. _____

Name _____ Date _____

Quiz 3 *(Lessons 1–7 through 1–8)*

Order each set of numbers from least to greatest.

1. 801, 598, 432, 439

2. 2.45, 2.09, 2.49, 2.94

3. 62.8, 61, 61.01, 62.47 61.008

4. 5.08, 4.99, 5.009, 5.20

5. 0.001, 0.010, 1.000, 1.10, 0.100

6. 348.42, 3.14, 34.842, 31.4, 34.824

Solve. Use the *guess and check* strategy.

7. John went to the park and saw 4 animals, ducks and dogs. If he saw a total of 14 legs, how many of each animal did he see?

8. Emma saw 22 legs on a total of 7 dogs and birds in the park. How many birds and how many dogs did she see?

1. _____

2. _____

3. _____

4. _____

5. _____

6. _____

7. _____

8. _____

Assessment

Name _____ Date _____

Mid-Chapter Test (Lessons 1–1 through 1–4)

1. In which number does 4 have a value of 40,000?

   A. 345,629   **C.** 532,471
   B. 429,376   **D.** 4,720,890

   1. _____

2. What is the expanded form of 340,729?

   F. 30,000 + 4,000 + 700 + 20 + 9
   G. 300,000 + 4,000 + 700 + 20 + 9
   H. 300,000 + 40,000 + 700 + 20 + 9
   J. 30,000 + 40,000 + 700 + 20 + 9

   2. _____

3. What is the short word form of 5,894,296?

   A. 5 billion, 894 million, 296
   B. 5 million, 894 thousand, 296
   C. 5 million, 894 billion, 296 thousand
   D. 5 billion, 894 thousand, 296

   3. _____

4. □ > 5

   F. 3   **H.** 5
   G. 4   **J.** 6

   4. _____

5. The distance to the sun is about 93,000,000 miles. How is this number written in words?

   A. ninety-three thousand   **C.** ninety-three billion
   B. ninety-three million   **D.** ninety-three trillion

   5. _____

6. How is $\frac{7}{10}$ written as a decimal?

   F. 0.007   **H.** 0.700
   G. 0.070   **J.** 7.000

   6. _____

7. Mrs. Jones bought 0.9 pound of turkey. What is this number as a fraction?

   A. $\frac{9}{1}$ **C.** $\frac{9}{100}$

   B. $\frac{9}{10}$ **D.** $\frac{9}{1,000}$

   7. _____

8. What is the place value of 3 in 735,229,981,412?

   8. _____

9. Write the short word form of 87,000,020.

   9. _____

Write each number in standard form.

10. seven hundred eighteen thousand, thirty-eight

    10. _____

11. 30,000,000 + 9,000,000 + 60,000 + 8,000 + 800 + 8

    11. _____

Name _____ Date _____

Vocabulary Test

Use the word list at the bottom of the page to complete each of the following statements.

Decimals that have the same value are _____.

_____

_____ is a system for writing numbers. In this system, the position of a digit determines its value.

_____

A _____ is a number that names part of a whole or group.

_____

The usual or common way to write a number is called _____.

_____

A _____ is any one of the numbers 0, 1, 2, 3…

_____

The way of writing a number as the sum of the *values* of its digits is called _____.

_____

A _____ is a number with one or more digits to the right of the decimal point.

_____

Word List

decimal
equivalent decimals
expanded form
fraction

place value
standard form
whole number

Name _____ Date _____

Oral Assessment

Read each question aloud to the student. Then write the student's answers on the lines below the question.

Write the number 879,456,231 where the student can see it.

1. What is the value of the 5 in this number?

_____

_____

2. What is the place value of the 8 in this number?

_____

_____

3. Which number is in the ten millions place?

_____

_____

4. Tell how you got your answer.

_____

_____

Oral Assessment *(continued)*

Write the number 12.637 where the student can see it.

5. What is the value of the 7 in this number?

_____

_____

6. What is the place value of the 3 in this number?

_____

_____

7. To order a set of numbers from greatest to least, what would you do?

_____

_____

Assessment

Chapter Project Rubric

Score	Explanation
3	Student successfully completed the chapter project. Student demonstrated appropriate use of chapter information in completing the chapter project.
2	Student completed the chapter project with partial success. Student partially demonstrated appropriate use of chapter information in completing the chapter project.
1	Student completed the chapter projects with little success. Student demonstrated very little appropriate use of chapter information in completing the chapter project.
0	Student did not complete the chapter project. Student demonstrated inappropriate use of chapter information in completing the chapter project.

Name _____ Date _____

1

Chapter Foldables® Rubric

Use Place Value

Pocket Chart Foldables

Score	Explanation
3	Student properly assembled Foldables® graphic organizer according to instructions.
	Student recorded information related to the chapter in the manner directed by the Foldables graphic organizer.
	Student used the Foldables graphic organizer as a study guide and organizational tool.
2	Student exhibited partial understanding of proper Foldables graphic organizer assembly.
	Student recorded most but not all information related to the chapter in the manner directed by the Foldables graphic organizer.
	Student demonstrated partial use of the Foldables graphic organizer as a study guide and organizational tool.
1	Student showed little understanding of proper Foldables graphic organizer assembly.
	Student recorded only some information related to the chapter in the manner directed by the Foldables graphic organizer.
	Student demonstrated little use of the Foldables graphic organizer as a study guide and organizational tool.
0	Student did not assemble Foldables graphic organizer according to instructions.
	Student recorded little or no information related to the chapter in the manner directed by the Foldables graphic organizer.
	Student did not use the Foldables graphic organizer as a study guide and organizational tool.

Assessment

Name _____ Date _____

Chapter Test, Form 1

Read each question carefully. Write your answer on the line provided.

1. In which number does 7 have a value of 700,000?

   A. 375,629   **B.** 729,326   **C.** 532,871   **D.** 7,620,890   1. _____

2. What is the expanded form of 280,734?   2. _____

   F. 20,000 + 8,000 + 700 + 30 + 4
   G. 200,000 + 8,000 + 700 + 30 + 4
   H. 200,000 + 80,000 + 700 + 30 + 4
   J. 20,000 + 80,000 + 700 + 30 + 4

3. The speed of light is about one hundred eighty-six thousand miles   3. _____
   per hour. What is this number?

   A. 18,600   **C.** 1,860,000
   B. 186,000   **D.** 18,600,000

4. $\square < 6$ 4. _____

   F. 5   **G.** 6   **H.** 7   **J.** 8

5. $\square < 0.011$ 5. _____

   A. 0.009   **B.** 0.011   **C.** 0.100   **D.** 0.110

6. $\square = 298.660$ 6. _____

   F. 289.660   **G.** 289.66   **H.** 298.600   **J.** 298.66

7. What is 4,984,296 written in short word form?   7. _____

   A. 4 billion, 984 million, 296   **C.** 4 million, 984 billion, 296 thousand
   B. 4 million, 984 thousand, 296   **D.** 4 billion, 984 thousand, 296

8. How is $\frac{6}{10}$ written as a decimal?   8. _____

   F. 0.006   **G.** 0.600   **H.** 0.060   **J.** 6.000

9. How is $\frac{17}{1,000}$ written as a decimal?   9. _____

   A. 17.000   **B.** 1.700   **C.** 0.170   **D.** 0.017

10. How is $\frac{873}{1,000}$ written as a decimal?   10. _____

    F. 0.873   **G.** 8.730   **H.** 87.300   **J.** 873.000

11. Mrs. Martinez bought 0.8 pound of turkey. What is this number as a   11. _____
    fraction?

    A. $\frac{8}{1}$ **C.** $\frac{8}{100}$

    B. $\frac{8}{10}$ **D.** $\frac{8}{1,000}$

12. What is 0.47 as a fraction?   12. _____

    F. $\frac{47}{1}$ **G.** $\frac{47}{10}$ **H.** $\frac{47}{100}$ **J.** $\frac{47}{1,000}$

13. What is 0.023 as a fraction?   13. _____

    A. $\frac{23}{1}$ **B.** $\frac{23}{10}$ **C.** $\frac{23}{100}$ **D.** $\frac{23}{1,000}$

14. What part of the model is shaded?   14. _____

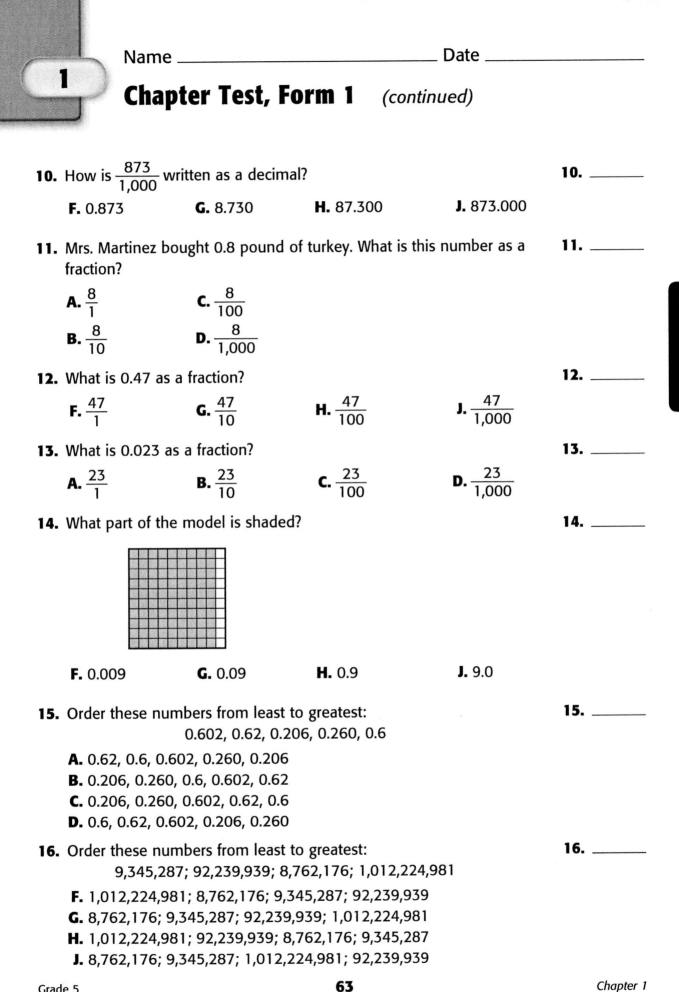

    F. 0.009   **G.** 0.09   **H.** 0.9   **J.** 9.0

15. Order these numbers from least to greatest: 15. _____
            0.602, 0.62, 0.206, 0.260, 0.6

    A. 0.62, 0.6, 0.602, 0.260, 0.206
    B. 0.206, 0.260, 0.6, 0.602, 0.62
    C. 0.206, 0.260, 0.602, 0.62, 0.6
    D. 0.6, 0.62, 0.602, 0.206, 0.260

16. Order these numbers from least to greatest: 16. _____
        9,345,287; 92,239,939; 8,762,176; 1,012,224,981

    F. 1,012,224,981; 8,762,176; 9,345,287; 92,239,939
    G. 8,762,176; 9,345,287; 92,239,939; 1,012,224,981
    H. 1,012,224,981; 92,239,939; 8,762,176; 9,345,287
    J. 8,762,176; 9,345,287; 1,012,224,981; 92,239,939

Name _____ Date _____

Chapter Test, Form 2A

Read each question carefully. Write your answer on the line provided.

1. In which number does 8 have a value of 800,000?

   A. 385,629   **B.** 532,871   **C.** 829,376   **D.** 8,720,590   **1.** _____

2. What is the expanded form of 560,732?

   F. 50,000 + 6,000 + 700 + 30 + 2
   G. 500,000 + 6,000 + 700 + 30 + 2
   H. 500,000 + 60,000 + 700 + 30 + 2
   J. 50,000 + 60,000 + 700 + 30 + 2   **2.** _____

3. The distance to Saturn is about 821,000,000 miles. How is this number written in words?

   A. eight hundred twenty-one thousand
   B. eight hundred twenty-one million
   C. eight hundred twenty-one billion
   D. eight hundred twenty-one trillion   **3.** _____

4. $\square < 7$

   F. 6   **G.** 7   **H.** 8   **J.** 9   **4.** _____

5. $\square < 0.022$

   A. 0.009   **B.** 0.022   **C.** 0.200   **D.** 0.220   **5.** _____

6. $\square = 348.660$

   F. 384.660   **G.** 384.66   **H.** 348.600   **J.** 348.66   **6.** _____

7. What is 1,584,296 written in short word form?

   A. 1 billion, 584 million, 296   **C.** 1 million, 584 billion, 296 thousand
   B. 1 million, 584 thousand, 296   **D.** 1 billion, 584 thousand, 296   **7.** _____

8. How is $\frac{3}{10}$ written as a decimal?

   F. 0.003   **G.** 0.300   **H.** 0.030   **J.** 3.000   **8.** _____

9. How is $\frac{16}{1,000}$ written as a decimal?
   A. 16.000   **B.** 1.600   **C.** 0.160   **D.** 0.016   **9.** _____

10. How is $\frac{871}{1,000}$ written as a decimal?
    F. 0.871   **G.** 8.710   **H.** 87.100   **J.** 871.000   **10.** _____

Chapter Test, Form 2A *(continued)*

11. Mrs. Smith bought 0.7 pound of turkey. What is this number as a fraction?

    A. $\frac{7}{1}$ 　　　**B.** $\frac{7}{100}$ 　　　**C.** $\frac{7}{10}$ 　　　**D.** $\frac{7}{1,000}$ 　　　**11.** _____

12. What is 0.67 as a fraction?

    F. $\frac{67}{1}$ 　　　**G.** $\frac{67}{10}$ 　　　**H.** $\frac{67}{100}$ 　　　**J.** $\frac{67}{1,000}$ 　　　**12.** _____

13. What is 0.093 as a fraction?

    A. $\frac{93}{1}$ 　　　**B.** $\frac{93}{10}$ 　　　**C.** $\frac{93}{100}$ 　　　**D.** $\frac{93}{1,000}$ 　　　**13.** _____

14. What part of the model is shaded? 　　　　　　　　　　　　**14.** _____

    F. 0.005 　　　**G.** 0.05 　　　**H.** 0.5 　　　**J.** 5.0

15. Order these numbers from least to greatest: 　　　　　　　**15.** _____
    0.302, 0.32, 0.106, 0.160, 0.3

    A. 0.32, 0.3, 0.302, 0.160, 0.106
    B. 0.106, 0.160, 0.3, 0.302, 0.32
    C. 0.106, 0.160, 0.302, 0.32, 0.3
    D. 0.3, 0.32, 0.302, 0.106, 0.160

16. Order these numbers from least to greatest: 　　　　　　　**16.** _____
    9,345,287; 92,239,939; 8,762,176; 1,012,224,981

    F. 1,012,224,981; 8,762,176; 9,345,287; 92,239,939
    G. 8,762,176; 9,345,287; 92,239,939; 1,012,224,981
    H. 1,012,224,981; 92,239,939; 8,762,176; 9,345,287
    J. 8,762,176; 9,345,287; 1,012,224,981; 92,239,939

Name _____ Date _____

Chapter Test, Form 2B

Read each question carefully. Write your answer on the line provided.

1. Where does 8 have a value of 800,000?

   A. 385,629   **B.** 829,376   **C.** 8,720,590

   1. _____

2. What is the expanded form of 560,732?

   F. 50,000 + 6,000 + 700 + 30 + 2
   G. 500,000 + 6,000 + 700 + 30 + 2
   H. 500,000 + 60,000 + 700 + 30 + 2

   2. _____

3. The sun is 93,000,000 miles away. What is this number in words?

   A. ninety-three thousand
   B. ninety-three million
   C. ninety-three billion

   3. _____

4. □ < 7

   F. 6   **G.** 7   **H.** 8

   4. _____

5. □ < 0.022

   A. 0.009   **B.** 0.022   **C.** 0.200

   5. _____

6. □ = 348.660

   F. 384.660   **G.** 384.66   **H.** 348.66

   6. _____

7. What is the short word form of 1,584,296?

   A. 1 billion, 584 million, 296
   B. 1 million, 584 thousand, 296
   C. 1 million, 584 billion, 296 thousand

   7. _____

8. Write $\frac{3}{10}$ as a decimal.

   F. 0.003   **H.** 0.030   **G.** 0.300

   8. _____

9. Write $\frac{16}{1,000}$ as a decimal.

   A. 16.000   **B.** 0.160   **C.** 0.016

   9. _____

10. Write $\frac{871}{1,000}$ as a decimal.

    F. 0.871   **G.** 8.710   **H.** 87.100

    10. _____

Assessment

11. Mrs. Smith bought 0.7 pound of ham. Write the number as a fraction.

   A. $\frac{7}{1}$ **B.** $\frac{7}{100}$ **C.** $\frac{7}{10}$

   11. _____

12. What is 0.67 as a fraction?

   F. $\frac{67}{1}$ **G.** $\frac{67}{10}$ **H.** $\frac{67}{100}$

   12. _____

13. What is 0.093 as a fraction?

   A. $\frac{93}{10}$ **B.** $\frac{93}{100}$ **C.** $\frac{93}{1,000}$

   13. _____

14. What part is shaded?

   F. 0.005   **G.** 0.05   **H.** 0.5

   14. _____

15. Order these numbers from least to greatest:
   0.302, 0.32, 0.106, 0.160, 0.3

   A. 0.32, 0.3, 0.302, 0.160, 0.106
   B. 0.106, 0.160, 0.3, 0.302, 0.32
   C. 0.106, 0.160, 0.302, 0.32, 0.3

   15. _____

16. Order these numbers from least to greatest:
   9,345,287; 92,239,939; 8,762,176; 1,012,224,981

   F. 1,012,224,981; 8,762,176; 9,345,287; 92,239,939
   G. 8,762,176; 9,345,287; 92,239,939; 1,012,224,981
   H. 1,012,224,981; 92,239,939; 8,762,176; 9,345,287

   16. _____

Name _____ Date _____

Chapter Test, Form 2C

Read each question carefully. Write your answer on the line provided.

1. Write the value of 8 in the number 829,376.

2. Write the value of 5 in the number 2.095.

3. Write the place value of 6 in 60,543,221.

4. Write the place value of 4 in 0.034.

5. Write the expanded form of 560,732.

6. The distance to Saturn is about 821,000,000 miles. Write this number in words.

Replace each □ with <, >, or = to make a true sentence.

7. 15 □ 10

8. 4,639 □ 4,638

9. 0.70 □ 0.700

10. Write the word form of 1,584,296.

1. _____

2. _____

3. _____

4. _____

5. _____

6. _____

7. _____

8. _____

9. _____

10. _____

Chapter Test, Form 2C   *(continued)*

11. Write $\frac{3}{10}$ as a decimal.

11. _____

12. Write $\frac{16}{1,000}$ as a decimal.

12. _____

13. Write $\frac{871}{1,000}$ as a decimal.

13. _____

14. Mrs. Smith bought 0.7 pound of turkey. Write this number as a fraction.

14. _____

15. Write 0.67 as a fraction.

15. _____

16. Write 0.093 as a fraction.

16. _____

17. What part of the model is shaded?

17. _____

18. Order these numbers from least to greatest:
    0.302, 0.32, 0.106, 0.160, 0.3

18. _____

19. Order these numbers from least to greatest:
    9,345,287; 92,239,939; 8,762,176; 1,012,224,981

19. _____

Assessment

Name _____ Date _____

Chapter Test, Form 2D

Read each question carefully. Write your answer on the line provided.

1. Write the value of 8 in 829,376.

2. Write the value of 5 in 2.095.

3. Write the place value of 6 in 60,543,221.

4. Write the place value of 4 in 0.034.

5. Write the expanded form of 560,732.

6. The sun is 93,000,000 miles away. What is this number in words?

Replace each □ with <, >, or = to make it true.

7. 15 □ 10

8. 4,639 □ 4,638

9. 0.70 □ 0.700

10. Write the short word form of 1,584,296.

1. _____

2. _____

3. _____

4. _____

5. _____

6. _____

7. _____

8. _____

9. _____

10. _____

11. Write $\dfrac{3}{10}$ as a decimal.

11. _____

12. Write $\dfrac{16}{1,000}$ as a decimal.

12. _____

13. Write $\dfrac{871}{1,000}$ as a decimal.

13. _____

14. Mrs. Smith bought 0.7 pound of ham. Write the number as a fraction.

14. _____

15. Write 0.67 as a fraction.

16. Write 0.093 as a fraction.

15. _____

17. What part is shaded?

16. _____

17. _____

18. Order from least to greatest:
     0.302, 0.32, 0.106, 0.160, 0.3

18. _____

19. Order from least to greatest:
     9,345,287; 92,239,939; 8,762,176; 1,012,224,981

19. _____

Name _____ Date _____

Chapter Test, Form 3

Read each question carefully. Write your answer on the line provided.

1. Write the value of 8 in the number 829,376.

2. Write the value of 5 in the number 2.095.

3. Write the place value of 6 in 60,543,221.

4. Write the place value of 4 in 0.034.

5. Write the expanded form of 560,732.

6. The distance to Saturn from Earth is about 821,000,000 miles. How is this number written in words?

Replace each □ with <, >, or = to make a true sentence.

7. 15 □ 10

8. 4,639 □ 4,638

9. 0.70 □ 0.700

10. Write 1,584,296 in word form.

1. _____

2. _____

3. _____

4. _____

5. _____

6. _____

7. _____

8. _____

9. _____

10. _____

11. Write the fraction $\frac{3}{10}$ as a decimal.

12. Write the fraction $\frac{16}{1,000}$ as a decimal.

13. Write the fraction $\frac{871}{1,000}$ as a decimal.

14. Mrs. Smith purchased 0.7 pound of smoked turkey. How is this number written as a fraction?

15. Write the decimal 0.67 as a fraction.

16. Write the decimal 0.093 as a fraction.

17. What part of the model below is shaded?

18. Put the numbers in order from least to greatest: 0.302, 0.32, 0.106, 0.160, 0.3

19. Put the numbers in order from least to greatest: 9,345,287; 92,239,939; 8,762,176; 1,012,224,981

11. _____

12. _____

13. _____

14. _____

15. _____

16. _____

17. _____

18. _____

19. _____

Assessment

1

Chapter Extended-Response Test

Demonstrate your knowledge by giving a clear, concise solution to each problem. Be sure to include all relevant drawings and justify your answers. You may show your solution in more than one way or investigate beyond the requirements of the problem. If necessary, record your answer on another piece of paper.

1. Name the four steps of the problem-solving plan in order. Tell what you do at each step.

_____

_____

_____

_____

2. Tell how to order whole numbers and decimals.

_____

_____

_____

3. Explain how to write 5.312 in expanded form.

_____

_____

Name _____ Date _____

Test Example

Travis is planning to try out for the track team The table below shows the number of miles he ran each day over the past 4 weeks. If the pattern continues, how many miles will he run during week 5?

Week	1	2	3	4	5
Miles	4	6	8	10	?

    A. 10 miles   **C.** 12 miles
    B. 11 miles   **D.** 13 miles

Read the Question.

You need to look for a pattern in the table to find the number of miles during week 5.

Solve the Question.

Find the increase in miles between each of the first 4 weeks.

$6 - 4 = 2$
$8 - 6 = 2$
$10 - 8 = 2$

The number of miles per day increases by 2 each week. So, during the fifth week, Travis will run $10 + 2 = 12$.
The answer is C.

Choose the best answer.

1. The number of people waiting for a movie is shown below. If the pattern continues, how many people will be waiting at 8:30?

Time	7:45	8:00	8:15	8:30
People Waiting	25	35	45	?

  A. 45   **B.** 50   **C.** 55   **D.** 6   **1.** _____

2. Which digit is in the ten thousands place in the number 4,832,561?

  F. 8   **G.** 3   **H.** 6   **J.** 4   **2.** _____

Cumulative Test Practice *(continued)*

3. A hundredths chart is shown with 0.73 shaded. Which fractional part of the cube is shaded?

3. _____

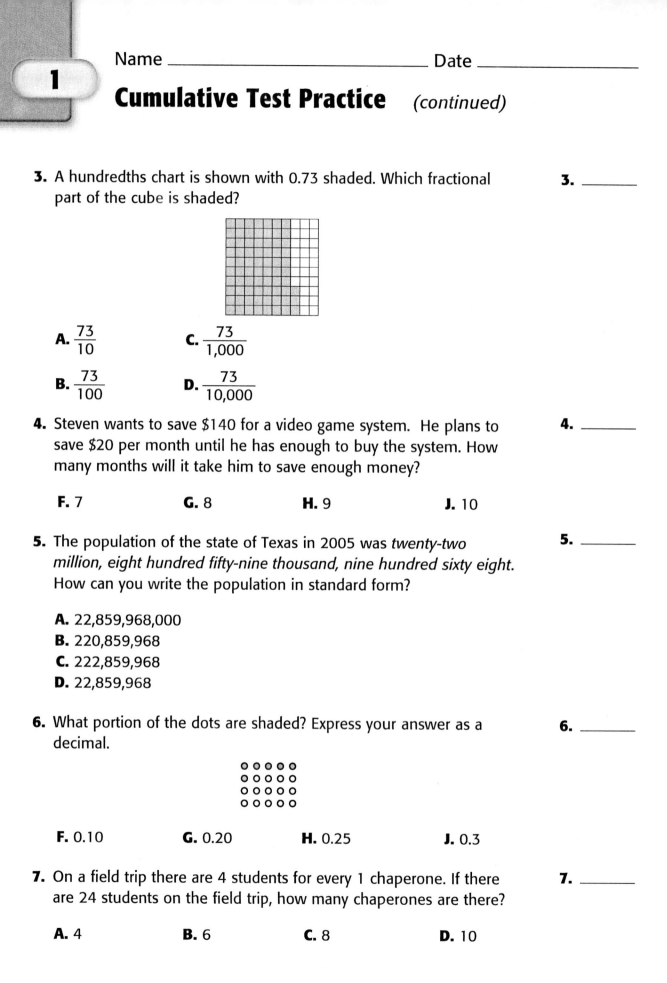

A. $\dfrac{73}{10}$

C. $\dfrac{73}{1,000}$

B. $\dfrac{73}{100}$

D. $\dfrac{73}{10,000}$

4. Steven wants to save $140 for a video game system. He plans to save $20 per month until he has enough to buy the system. How many months will it take him to save enough money?

4. _____

F. 7   **G.** 8   **H.** 9   **J.** 10

5. The population of the state of Texas in 2005 was *twenty-two million, eight hundred fifty-nine thousand, nine hundred sixty eight*. How can you write the population in standard form?

5. _____

A. 22,859,968,000
B. 220,859,968
C. 222,859,968
D. 22,859,968

6. What portion of the dots are shaded? Express your answer as a decimal.

6. _____

○ ○ ○ ○ ○
○ ○ ○ ○ ○
○ ○ ○ ○ ○
○ ○ ○ ○ ○

F. 0.10   **G.** 0.20   **H.** 0.25   **J.** 0.3

7. On a field trip there are 4 students for every 1 chaperone. If there are 24 students on the field trip, how many chaperones are there?

7. _____

A. 4   **B.** 6   **C.** 8   **D.** 10

1

Cumulative Test Practice *(continued)*

8. How would you read the price of a pencil at the bookstore as
   a decimal?

Bookstore Prices	
Pencil	$0.25
Eraser	$ 0.15

   F. fifteen tenths   **H.** twenty-five tenths
   G. fifteen hundredths   **J.** twenty-five hundredths

8. _____

9. Which decimal represents the shaded portion of the design?

   A. 0.48   **B.** 0.408   **C.** 0.048   **D.** 0.0048

9. _____

10. The table shows the times of four runners. Which of the following
    shows the times in order from fastest to slowest?

12.31
12.03
12.30
11.99

    F. 11.99, 12.03, 12.30, 12.31   **H.** 12.31, 11.99, 12.30, 12.03
    G. 11.99, 12.30, 12.03, 12.31   **J.** 12.31, 12.30, 12.03, 11.99

10. _____

11. A carpenter needs to cut a board with a length of twenty five and
    forty-four hundredths inches. How can you write *twenty five and
    forty-four hundredths* as a decimal?

11. _____

12. Write the number 3,460,301 in expanded form.

12. _____

13. Kelly bought a snack for $3.85 and paid with a $5 bill. Her change
    included nine coins, including three quarters, two dimes, and four
    other coins. What is the value of each of the other four coins?

13. _____

Assessment

Name _____ Date _____

Student Recording Sheet

Use this recording sheet with pages 56–57 of the Student Edition.

Read each question. Then fill in the correct answer.

1. Ⓐ Ⓑ Ⓒ Ⓓ

2. Ⓕ Ⓖ Ⓗ Ⓙ

3. Ⓐ Ⓑ Ⓒ Ⓓ

4. Ⓕ Ⓖ Ⓗ Ⓙ

5. Ⓐ Ⓑ Ⓒ Ⓓ

6. _____

7. _____

8. _____

   _____

   _____

9. _____

   _____

   _____

Answers (Graphic Organizer and Anticipation Guide)

Name _____ Date _____

1 **Anticipation Guide**

Place Value and Number Sense

STEP 1 **Before you begin Chapter 1**

- Read each statement.
- Decide whether you agree (A) or disagree (D) with the statement.
- Write A or D in the first column OR if you are not sure whether you agree or disagree, write NS (Not Sure).

STEP 1 A, D, or NS	Statement	STEP 2 A or D
	1. The value of the 7 in the number 3,731,002 is 70,000	D
	2. 5,692,001 > 5,692,000	A
	3. The standard form of 39 thousand, 15 is 3,915	D
	4. $\frac{87}{1,000} = 0.087$	A
	5. The value of the 7 in the number 0.017 is 0.007	A
	6. 0.990 = 0.99	A

STEP 2 **After you complete Chapter 1**

- Reread each statement and complete the last column by entering an A (agree) or a D (disagree).
- Did any of your opinions about the statements change from the first column?
- For those statements that you mark with a D, use a separate sheet of paper to explain why you disagree. Use examples, if possible.

Name _____ Date _____

1 **Graphic Organizer**

Use this graphic organizer to take notes on **Chapter 1: Use Place Value.** Fill in the missing information.

Type of Number	Definition	Examples
Word Form	A way of writing a number that only uses words.	1,015 = one thousand, fifteen
Standard Form	The usual way of writing a number that shows only its digits, no words.	4,376
Expanded Form	The representation of a number as a sum that shows the value of each digit.	536 = 500 + 30 + 6

Chapter Resources

Answers

Answers (Lesson 1–1)

Name _____ Date _____

1-1 Skills Practice

Place Value Through Billions

Name the place value and write the value of the underlined digit.

1. 2,346 — **tens; 40**
2. 65,893 — **thousands; 5,000**
3. 763,406,594 — **ten millions; 60,000,000**
4. 407,356,138,920 — **billions; 7,000,000,000**
5. 64,321,008 — **hundred thousands; 300,000**
6. 117,927,724,417 — **ten billions; 10,000,000,000**
7. 903,004,200,006 — **millions; 4,000,000**

Write each number in standard form.

8. 3 thousand, 125 — **3,125**
9. 52 thousand, 40 — **52,040**

Write each number in expanded form.

10. 7,450,693 — **7,000,000 + 400,000 + 50,000 + 600 + 90 + 3**
11. 531,017 — **500,000 + 30,000 + 1,000 + 10 + 7**

Write each number in word form.

12. 9,000,000,006 — **nine billion, six**
13. 273,273 — **two hundred seventy-three thousand, two hundred seventy-three**

Solve.

14. Mercury is the planet closest to the Sun. It orbits the Sun from a distance of about 28 million, 600 thousand miles. Write the number in standard form.

    28,600,000 miles

15. Neptune is the planet farthest from the Sun. It orbits the Sun from a distance of about 4 billion, 497 million miles. Write the number in standard form.

    4,497,000,000 miles

Name _____ Date _____

1-1 Reteach

Place Value Through Billions

A place-value chart can help you read greater numbers. Say the number in each period followed by the name of the period, except for the ones.

Billions Period			Millions Period			Thousands Period			Ones Period		
H	T	O	H	T	O	H	T	O	H	T	O
	4	7	3	0	2	0	1	6	2	9	4

Standard form: 47,302,016,294

Word form: 47 **billion**, 302 **million**, 16 **thousand**, 294
Read: forty-seven billion, three hundred two million, sixteen thousand, two hundred ninety-four

Expanded form: 40,000,000,000 + 7,000,000,000 + 300,000,000 + 2,000,000 + 10,000 + 6,000 + 200 + 90 + 4

Write the word form and the expanded form of each number. For help, complete the place-value chart.

1.

Billions Period			Millions Period			Thousands Period			Ones Period		
H	T	O	H	T	O	H	T	O	H	T	O
				2	7	0	0	6	5	9	3

Standard form: 27,006,593

Word form: **twenty-seven million, six thousand, five hundred ninety-three**

Expanded form: **20,000,000 + 7,000,000 + 6,000 + 500 + 90 + 3**

2. Standard form: 6,020,700,510 **six billion, twenty million,**

Word form: **seven hundred thousand, five hundred ten**

Expanded form: **6,000,000,000 + 20,000,000 + 700,000 + 500 + 10**

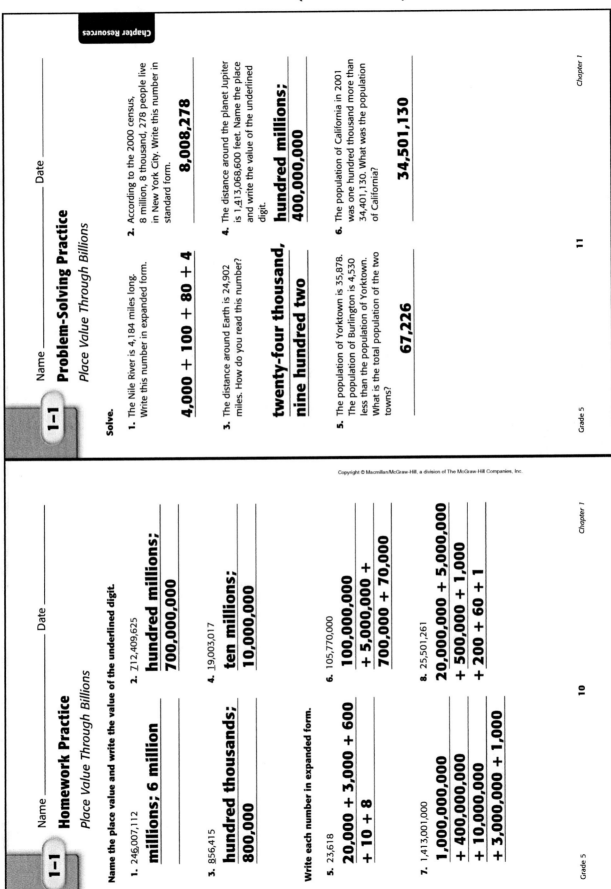

1-1

Name _____ Date _____

Homework Practice
Place Value Through Billions

Name the place value and write the value of the underlined digit.

1. 246,007,112
millions; 6 million

2. 712,409,625
hundred millions;
700,000,000

3. 856,415
hundred thousands;
800,000

4. 19,003,017
ten millions;
10,000,000

Write each number in expanded form.

5. 23,618
20,000 + 3,000 + 600
+ 10 + 8

6. 105,770,000
100,000,000
+ 5,000,000 +
700,000 + 70,000

7. 1,413,001,000
1,000,000,000
+ 400,000,000
+ 10,000,000
+ 3,000,000 + 1,000

8. 25,501,261
20,000,000 + 5,000,000
+ 500,000 + 1,000
+ 200 + 60 + 1

1-1

Name _____ Date _____

Problem-Solving Practice
Place Value Through Billions

Solve.

1. The Nile River is 4,184 miles long. Write this number in expanded form.

4,000 + 100 + 80 + 4

2. According to the 2000 census, 8 million, 8 thousand, 278 people live in New York City. Write this number in standard form.

8,008,278

3. The distance around Earth is 24,902 miles. How do you read this number?

twenty-four thousand,
nine hundred two

4. The distance around the planet Jupiter is 1,413,068,600 feet. Name the place and write the value of the underlined digit.

hundred millions;
400,000,000

5. The population of Yorktown is 35,878. The population of Burlington is 4,530 less than the population of Yorktown. What is the total population of the two towns?

67,226

6. The population of California in 2001 was one hundred thousand more than 34,401,130. What was the population of California?

34,501,130

Answers (Lessons 1–1 and 1–2)

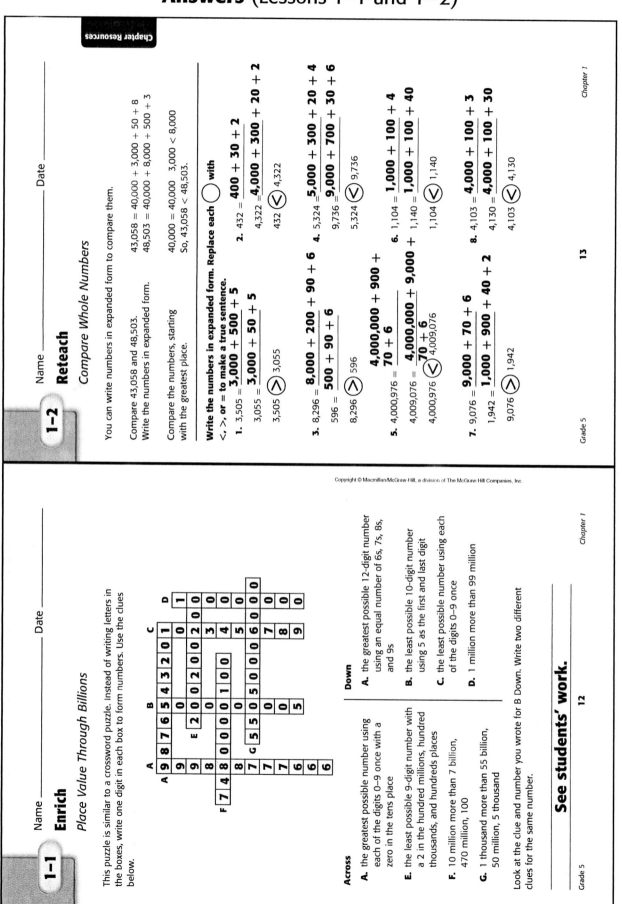

1-2 Reteach

Name _____ Date _____

Compare Whole Numbers

You can write numbers in expanded form to compare them.

Compare 43,058 and 48,503.
Write the numbers in expanded form.

$43{,}058 = 40{,}000 + 3{,}000 + 50 + 8$
$48{,}503 = 40{,}000 + 8{,}000 + 500 + 3$

Compare the numbers, starting with the greatest place.

$40{,}000 = 40{,}000 \quad 3{,}000 < 8{,}000$
So, $43{,}058 < 48{,}503$.

Write the numbers in expanded form. Replace each ◯ with <, >, or = to make a true sentence.

1. $3{,}505 = \underline{3{,}000 + 500 + 5}$
   $3{,}055 = \underline{3{,}000 + 50 + 5}$
   $3{,}505 \;>\; 3{,}055$

2. $432 = \underline{400 + 30 + 2}$
   $4{,}322 = \underline{4{,}000 + 300 + 20 + 2}$
   $432 \;<\; 4{,}322$

3. $8{,}296 = \underline{8{,}000 + 200 + 90 + 6}$
   $596 = \underline{500 + 90 + 6}$
   $8{,}296 \;>\; 596$

4. $5{,}324 = \underline{5{,}000 + 300 + 20 + 4}$
   $9{,}736 = \underline{9{,}000 + 700 + 30 + 6}$
   $5{,}324 \;<\; 9{,}736$

5. $4{,}000{,}976 = \underline{4{,}000{,}000 + 900 + 70 + 6}$
   $4{,}009{,}076 = \underline{4{,}000{,}000 + 9{,}000 + 70 + 6}$
   $4{,}000{,}976 \;<\; 4{,}009{,}076$

6. $1{,}104 = \underline{1{,}000 + 100 + 4}$
   $1{,}140 = \underline{1{,}000 + 100 + 40}$
   $1{,}104 \;<\; 1{,}140$

7. $9{,}076 = \underline{9{,}000 + 70 + 6}$
   $1{,}942 = \underline{1{,}000 + 900 + 40 + 2}$
   $9{,}076 \;>\; 1{,}942$

8. $4{,}103 = \underline{4{,}000 + 100 + 3}$
   $4{,}130 = \underline{4{,}000 + 100 + 30}$
   $4{,}103 \;<\; 4{,}130$

Grade 5   13   Chapter 1

1-1 Enrich

Name _____ Date _____

Place Value Through Billions

This puzzle is similar to a crossword puzzle. Instead of writing letters in the boxes, write one digit in each box to form numbers. Use the clues below.

Across

A. the greatest possible number using each of the digits 0–9 once with a zero in the tens place

E. the least possible 9-digit number with a 2 in the hundred millions, hundred thousands, and hundreds places

F. 10 million more than 7 billion, 470 million, 100

G. 1 thousand more than 55 billion, 50 million, 5 thousand

Down

A. the greatest possible 12-digit number using an equal number of 6s, 7s, 8s, and 9s

B. the least possible 10-digit number using 5 as the first and last digit

C. the least possible number using each of the digits 0–9 once

D. 1 million more than 99 million

Look at the clue and number you wrote for B Down. Write two different clues for the same number.

See students' work.

Grade 5   12   Chapter 1

Answers (Lesson 1–2)

1-2 Skills Practice

Name _____ Date _____

Skills Practice
Compare Whole Numbers

Replace each ◯ **with <, >, or = to make a true sentence.**

1. 1,040 (>) 10
2. 14,092 (<) 19,812
3. 840 (>) 480
4. 1,001 (>) 101
5. 123,778 (=) 123,778
6. 9,879 (>) 9,798
7. 6,823 (>) 682
8. 5 (<) 13
9. 190 (>) 19
10. 71 (<) 98
11. 192 (<) 291
12. 611 (=) 611
13. 314 (<) 3,140
14. 657 (>) 567
15. 324 (<) 452

16. Michael ran 7 miles during one week. Krista ran 9 miles during one week. Who ran more miles?
Krista

17. Jerry is 55 inches tall. Tom is 56 inches tall. Who is taller?
Tom

1-2 Homework Practice

Name _____ Date _____

Homework Practice
Compare Whole Numbers

Replace each ◯ **with <, >, or = to make a true sentence.**

1. 2,040 (>) 20
2. 13,052 (<) 16,912
3. 201 (<) 2,001
4. 433,778 (=) 433,778
5. 6,321 (>) 282
6. 9 (<) 13
7. 31 (<) 38
8. 912 (<) 921
9. 334 (<) 3,340
10. 657 (>) 567

Write the numbers in expanded form. Replace each ◯ **with <, >, or = to make a true sentence.**

11. $3,412 = 3,000 + 400 + 10 + 2$
    $3,421 = 3,000 + 400 + 20 + 1$
    3,412 (<) 3,421

12. $932 = 900 + 30 + 2$
    $9,322 = 9,000 + 300 + 20 + 2$
    932 (<) 9,322

Spiral Review
Write each number in standard form. (Lesson 1–1)

13. 11 million, 106 thousand, 300
    11,106,300

14. 91 billion, 13 million, 70 thousand, 2
    91,013,070,002

15. 300,000 + 20,000 + 300 + 70 + 8
    320,378

16. 1,000,000 + 50,000 + 9,000 + 4
    1,059,004

Answers

Answers (Lesson 1–2)

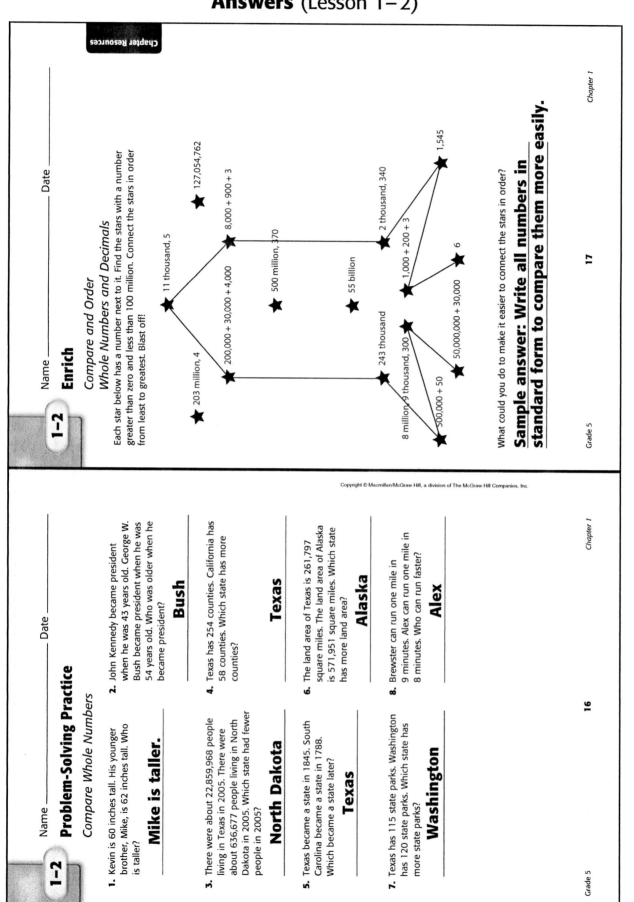

1–2

Name _____ Date _____

Problem-Solving Practice

Compare Whole Numbers

1. Kevin is 60 inches tall. His younger brother, Mike, is 62 inches tall. Who is taller?

   Mike is taller.

2. John Kennedy became president when he was 43 years old. George W. Bush became president when he was 54 years old. Who was older when he became president?

   Bush

3. There were about 22,859,968 people living in Texas in 2005. There were about 636,677 people living in North Dakota in 2005. Which state had fewer people in 2005?

   North Dakota

4. Texas has 254 counties. California has 58 counties. Which state has more counties?

   Texas

5. Texas became a state in 1845. South Carolina became a state in 1788. Which became a state later?

   Texas

6. The land area of Texas is 261,797 square miles. The land area of Alaska is 571,951 square miles. Which state has more land area?

   Alaska

7. Texas has 115 state parks. Washington has 120 state parks. Which state has more state parks?

   Washington

8. Brewster can run one mile in 9 minutes. Alex can run one mile in 8 minutes. Who can run faster?

   Alex

1–2

Name _____ Date _____

Enrich

Compare and Order
Whole Numbers and Decimals

Each star below has a number next to it. Find the stars with a number greater than zero and less than 100 million. Connect the stars in order from least to greatest. Blast off!

127,054,762

11 thousand, 5

8,000 + 900 + 3

200,000 + 30,000 + 4,000

500 million, 370

203 million, 4

55 billion

2 thousand, 340

1,000 + 200 + 3

1,545

6

50,000,000 + 30,000

243 thousand

8 million, 9 thousand, 300

500,000 + 50

What could you do to make it easier to connect the stars in order?

Sample answer: Write all numbers in standard form to compare them more easily.

1-3

Name _____ **Date** _____

Reteach

Problem-Solving Investigation: Use the Four-Step Plan

The three tallest buildings in Boston are the Prudential Tower (750 ft), the John Hancock Tower (790 ft), and the Federal Reserve Building (604 ft). List these buildings from tallest to shortest.

Step 1 Understand	**Be sure you understand the problem.** Read carefully. Identify what you need to do. • What do you know? **You know the height of each building.** • What have you been asked to do? **List some buildings from tallest to shortest.**
Step 2 Plan	**Plan a strategy.** You can compare the heights of the buildings. • Decide what actions you will take and in what order.
Step 3 Solve	**Solve the problem.** Follow your plan. Compare Prudential Tower and John Hancock Tower. 750 < 790 Compare Prudential Tower and the Federal Reserve Building. 750 > 604 The order from tallest to shortest is John Hancock Tower, Prudential Tower, Federal Reserve Building.
Step 4 Check	**Did you answer the question? Is the solution reasonable?** Yes, you have listed the buildings from tallest to shortest.

Solve. Use the four-step plan.

1. Scotia Plaza in Toronto is 902 feet tall. First Canadian Place in Toronto is 978 feet tall. Which building is taller?

First Canadian Place

2. Dallas' Renaissance Tower is 886 feet, Bank of America Plaza is 921 feet, and Bank One Center is 787 feet. List the buildings from shortest to tallest.

Bank One Center,

Renaissance Tower,

Bank of America Plaza

1-3

Name _____ **Date** _____

Reteach

Problem-Solving Investigation: Use the Four-Step Plan
(continued)

3. The Andersons are buying a paddle boat for $540. They plan to pay in four equal payments. How much will their payments be?

$135.00

4. Lynn can walk two miles in 24 minutes. At this rate, how long will it take her to walk 6 miles?

72 minutes

5. Bridgit plays on the basketball team. The table shows the number of baskets she made in the first three days of practice. If the pattern continues, how many baskets will she make on Thursday and Friday?

Day	Baskets
Monday	21
Tuesday	22
Wednesday	24
Thursday	**27**
Friday	**31**

6. The Glendale Plaza Building in Glendale, California is 353 feet tall. The U.S. Bank Tower in Los Angeles, California is 1,017 feet tall. Which building is taller?

The U.S. Bank Tower

7. After going on vacation, you come home with $5. You spent $6 on a pair of sunglasses, $10 on snacks, $4 on a book, and $5 on arcade games. How much money did you start with?

$30

Answers

Answers (Lesson 1–3)

1-3

Name _____ Date _____

Homework Practice

Problem-Solving Investigation: Use the Four-Step Plan

Use the four-step plan to solve each problem.

1. A train left the station at 12:45. It traveled 455 miles in 7 hours. How many miles did it travel in each hour?

   65 miles

2. The Delgados are buying a pool that is 30 feet x 30 feet for $1,188. They plan to pay in 12 equal payments. Find the amount of each payment.

   $99

3. After shopping for school supplies, Martin came home with $4. He bought a pack of pens for $6, a calculator for $12, and a notebook for $3. How much money did he start with?

   $25

4. Julio increases the laps he runs by three laps each day. If he begins on Monday by running 4 laps, how many laps will he run on Wednesday at his current rate?

   10 laps

Spiral Review

Replace each ◯ with <, >, or = to make a true sentence. (Lesson 1–2)

5. 17 ⊘> 8

6. 68 ⊘< 93

7. 121 ⊘< 1,210

8. 3,410 ⊘> 3,401

9. 17,681 ⊘> 16,681

10. 3,725,720 ⊘< 3,752,720

Grade 5   21   Chapter 1

1-3

Name _____ Date _____

Skills Practice

Problem-Solving Strategy: Use the Four-Step Plan

Solve. Use the four-step plan.

1. The three highest mountains in Colorado are Mount Massive (14,421 ft), Mount Harvard (14,420 ft), and Mount Elbert (14,433 ft). Which mountain has the greatest height?

   Mount Elbert

2. Hoover Dam, in the United States, is 223 meters high. Ertan Dam, in China, is 240 meters high. In Canada, Mica Dam is 243 meters high. List the dams by height from greatest to least.

   Mica Dam, Ertan Dam, Hoover Dam

3. The Akshi Kaikyo suspension bridge in Japan has a span of 6,570 feet. The Humber suspension bridge in England has a span of 4,626 feet. The Izmit Bay suspension bridge in Turkey has a span of 5,538 feet. Which bridge has the shortest span?

   Humber

5. List the tunnels in the table at the right by name in order from shortest to longest.

   Devil's Side, Squirrel Hill, Liberty Tubes, E. Johnson Memorial

Land Tunnels in the United States		
Tunnel	State	Length (ft)
Liberty Tubes	Pennsylvania	5,920
Devil's Side	California	3,400
E. Johnson Memorial	Colorado	8,959
Squirrel Hill	Pennsylvania	4,225

4. There are three long tunnels that go under Boston Harbor. The Sumner Tunnel is 5,653 feet long. The Callahan Tunnel is 5,070 feet long. The Ted Williams Tunnel is 8,448 feet long. List the tunnels from shortest to longest.

   Callahan Tunnel, Sumner Tunnel, Ted Williams Tunnel

Grade 5   20   Chapter 1

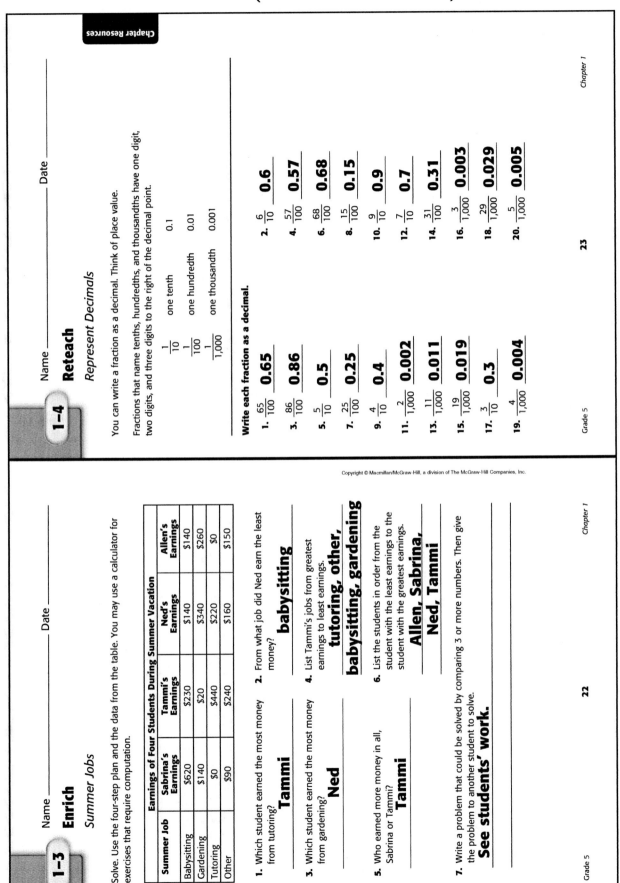

Chapter Resources

Name _____ Date _____

1-3 Enrich

Summer Jobs

Solve. Use the four-step plan and the data from the table. You may use a calculator for exercises that require computation.

Earnings of Four Students During Summer Vacation

Summer Job	Sabrina's Earnings	Tammi's Earnings	Ned's Earnings	Allen's Earnings
Babysitting	$620	$230	$140	$140
Gardening	$140	$20	$340	$260
Tutoring	$0	$440	$220	$0
Other	$90	$240	$160	$150

1. Which student earned the most money from tutoring?

Tammi

2. From what job did Ned earn the least money?

babysitting

3. Which student earned the most money from gardening?

Ned

4. List Tammi's jobs from greatest earnings to least earnings.

tutoring, other, babysitting, gardening

5. Who earned more money in all, Sabrina or Tammi?

Tammi

6. List the students in order from the student with the least earnings to the student with the greatest earnings.

Allen, Sabrina, Ned, Tammi

7. Write a problem that could be solved by comparing 3 or more numbers. Then give the problem to another student to solve.

See students' work.

Name _____ Date _____

1-4 Reteach

Represent Decimals

You can write a fraction as a decimal. Think of place value.

$\frac{1}{10}$	one tenth	0.1
$\frac{1}{100}$	one hundredth	0.01
$\frac{1}{1,000}$	one thousandth	0.001

Fractions that name tenths, hundredths, and thousandths have one digit, two digits, and three digits to the right of the decimal point.

Write each fraction as a decimal.

1. $\frac{65}{100}$ **0.65**

2. $\frac{6}{10}$ **0.6**

3. $\frac{86}{100}$ **0.86**

4. $\frac{57}{100}$ **0.57**

5. $\frac{5}{10}$ **0.5**

6. $\frac{68}{100}$ **0.68**

7. $\frac{25}{100}$ **0.25**

8. $\frac{15}{100}$ **0.15**

9. $\frac{4}{10}$ **0.4**

10. $\frac{9}{10}$ **0.9**

11. $\frac{2}{1,000}$ **0.002**

12. $\frac{7}{10}$ **0.7**

13. $\frac{11}{1,000}$ **0.011**

14. $\frac{31}{100}$ **0.31**

15. $\frac{19}{1,000}$ **0.019**

16. $\frac{3}{1,000}$ **0.003**

17. $\frac{3}{10}$ **0.3**

18. $\frac{29}{1,000}$ **0.029**

19. $\frac{4}{1,000}$ **0.004**

20. $\frac{5}{1,000}$ **0.005**

Answers

Answers (Lesson 1–4)

Skills Practice

Name _____ Date _____

1-4

Skills Practice

Represent Decimals

Write each fraction as a decimal.

1. $\frac{3}{10}$ **0.3**
2. $\frac{498}{1,000}$ **0.498**
3. $\frac{7}{10}$ **0.7**
4. $\frac{1}{10}$ **0.1**
5. $\frac{947}{1,000}$ **0.947**
6. $\frac{3}{10}$ **0.3**
7. $\frac{18}{20}$ **0.9**
8. $\frac{1}{50}$ **0.02**
9. $\frac{11}{20}$ **0.55**
10. $\frac{1}{10}$ **0.1**
11. $\frac{256}{1,000}$ **0.256**
12. $\frac{3}{100}$ **0.03**
13. $\frac{77}{100}$ **0.77**
14. $\frac{3}{100}$ **0.03**
15. $\frac{13}{50}$ **0.26**
16. $\frac{999}{1,000}$ **0.999**
17. $\frac{9}{50}$ **0.18**
18. $\frac{751}{1,000}$ **0.751**
19. $\frac{7}{10}$ **0.7**
20. $\frac{2}{10}$ **0.2**
21. $\frac{1}{20}$ **0.05**
22. $\frac{357}{1,000}$ **0.357**
23. $\frac{1}{20}$ **0.05**
24. $\frac{632}{1,000}$ **0.632**

Solve.

25. The largest butterfly in the world is found in Papua, New Guinea. The female of the species weighs about 0.9 ounce. Use a fraction to write the female's weight.

    $\frac{9}{10}$ **ounce**

26. The shortest fish ever recorded is the dwarf goby found in the Indo-Pacific. The female of this species is about 0.35 inch long. Use a fraction to write the female's length.

    $\frac{35}{100}$ **inch**

Homework Practice

Name _____ Date _____

1-4

Homework Practice

Represent Decimals

Write each fraction as a decimal.

1. $\frac{3}{5}$ **0.6**
2. $1\frac{1}{10}$ **1.1**
3. $\frac{37}{50}$ **0.74**
4. $\frac{29}{100}$ **0.29**
5. $\frac{127}{200}$ **0.635**
6. $\frac{1}{40}$ **0.025**
7. $6\frac{3}{10}$ **6.3**
8. $\frac{19}{20}$ **0.95**
9. $9\frac{1}{20}$ **9.05**
10. $8\frac{7}{10}$ **8.7**
11. $2\frac{7}{20}$ **2.35**
12. $\frac{477}{500}$ **0.954**
13. $\frac{129}{200}$ **0.645**
14. $\frac{391}{500}$ **0.782**
15. $\frac{493}{1,000}$ **0.493**

Spiral Review

Solve. Use the four-step plan. (Lesson 1-3)

16. There are 15 students going to the museum. If each student pays $7 for admission and $5 for lunch, what is the total cost for the 15 students?

    $180

17. Meredith worked on her sewing project for 45 minutes every night for 4 nights. She worked on the project for 30 minutes a night for the rest of the week. How many minutes did she work on her project altogether?

    270 minutes

Chapter Resources

Name _____ Date _____

1-4 Enrich

Grid Design

The grid area below is made up of 4 10-by-10 grids. Each 10-by-10 grid represents 1. Use three different color pencils or crayons to make a design on the grids. Color the grids completely.

Write a decimal to tell what area you shaded with each color. Remember, 100 boxes (one grid) represent 1. **See students' work.**

Color	Decimal

When was it necessary to write a decimal that included a whole number?

See students' work.

Name _____ Date _____

1-4 Problem-Solving Practice

Represent Decimals

Solve.

1. One cup is equal to 0.5 pint. Write this decimal as a fraction.

$$\frac{5}{10}$$

2. Aimee needs 0.25 cup of vegetable oil to make muffins. Write this decimal as a fraction.

$$\frac{25}{100}$$

3. Trudy is making a picture frame and needs nails that measure 0.375 of an inch. At the hardware store, nails are measured in fractions of an inch: $\frac{125}{1,000}$ inch, $\frac{25}{100}$ inch, and $\frac{375}{1,000}$ inch. Which of these nails should she buy?

$$\frac{375}{1,000}$$

4. At Richardson Elementary, 0.35 of the buses were late because of a snowstorm. Write the decimal as a fraction.

$$\frac{35}{100}$$

5. Neil needs several pieces of wood measuring $\frac{6}{10}$ foot each. The lumber store will cut pieces only in increments of 0.25 foot: 0.25 foot, 0.5 foot, 0.75 foot, and so on. Neil agrees to have the lumber store cut the pieces, but he will have to trim some off once he gets home. He wants to trim the least amount off each piece. Which measurement should the lumber store use to cut the pieces?

0.75 feet

6. A vitamin contains sixty-two thousandths gram of vitamin E and 0.038 gram of vitamin A. Does the vitamin contain at least twice the amount of vitamin E than vitamin A?

No

7. Of the books at the Public Library, $\frac{25}{100}$ are for young readers. What decimal names this fraction?

0.25

8. Kathleen has recorded 0.4 of a book on to a cassette tape. What fraction of the book has she recorded?

$$\frac{4}{10}$$

Answers

Answers (Lesson 1–5)

Name _____ Date _____

1-5 Skills Practice

Place Value Through Thousandths

Write the place value and the value of each underlined digit.

1. 2.8 **tenths; 0.8**   2. 1.42_7_ **thousandths; 0.007**

3. 2.5_3_1 **hundredths; 0.03**   4. 35.0_5_2 **tenths; 0**

5. 5.3_5_ **hundredths; 0.05**   6. 24.00_2_ **thousandths; 0.002**

Write each number in standard form.

7. 5 and 34 thousandths **5.034**

8. 34 and 12 hundredths **34.12**

9. 20 + 4 + 0.7 + 0.04 + 0.005 **24.745**

10. 100 + 7 + 0.05 + 0.007 **107.057**

Write each number in expanded form and word form.

11. 23.5 **20 + 3 + 0.5**
twenty-three and five tenths

12. 164.38 **100 + 60 + 4 + 0.3 + 0.08**
one hundred sixty-four and thirty-eight hundredths

13. 4.292 **4 + 0.2 + 0.09 + 0.002**
four and two hundred ninety-two thousandths

14. 53.007 **50 + 3 + 0.007**
fifty-three and seven thousandths

Name _____ Date _____

1-5 Reteach

Place Value Through Thousandths

The decimal 1.56 can be shown in several ways. The models below will show you different ways to represent 1.56.

You can use a place-value chart like the one below to represent 1.56.

1,000	100	10	1	0.1	0.01	0.001
Thousands	Hundreds	Tens	Ones	Tenths	Hundredths	Thousandths
0	0	0	1	5	6	

You can also represent 1.56 using a decimal model:

Represent the following decimals.

1. Use the place-value chart to show 0.87.

1,000	100	10	1	0.1	0.01	0.001
Thousands	Hundreds	Tens	Ones	Tenths	Hundredths	Thousandths
			0	**8**	**7**	

2. Use the decimal model to show 1.03.

1,000	100	10	1	0.1	0.01	0.001
Thousands	Hundreds	Tens	Ones	Tenths	Hundredths	Thousandths
0	**0**	**0**	**1**	**0**	**3**	**0**

Answers (Lesson 1–5)

1-5

Name _____ Date _____

Problem-Solving Practice
Place Value Through Thousandths

For Exercises 1–4, use the table.

The table shows lifetime batting averages for leading baseball players.

Lifetime Batting Averages for Leading Players

Player	Team	Batting Average
Tony Gwynn, Jr.	Milwaukee Brewers	0.294
Derek Jeter	New York Yankees	0.341
Ichiro Suzuki	Seattle Mariners	0.319
Mike Piazza	San Diego Padres	0.277
Chipper Jones	Atlanta Braves	0.318

Source: mlb.com

1. Write Mike Piazza's batting average in word form.

two hundred seventy-seven thousandths

2. Which digit is in the thousandths place of each player's batting average?

Gwynn–4; Jeter–1; Suzuki–9; Piazza–7; Jones–8

3. What is the batting average for the New York Yankees player in expanded form?

0.3 + 0.04 + 0.001

4. Which player's average has a 4 in the hundredths place?

Derek Jeter

5. When measuring board footage for some exotic woods, a carpenter must use 1.25 for thickness rather than 1 in her calculations. Write 1.25 in expanded form.

1.00 + 0.20 + 0.05

6. The summer camp Jason attends is exactly four hundred twenty-three and four tenths of a mile from his home. Write *four hundred twenty-three and four tenths* in standard form.

423.4

Grade 5   31   Chapter 1

1-5

Name _____ Date _____

Homework Practice
Place Value Through Thousandths

Write the place value and the value of each underlined digit.

1. 2.6<u>5</u>4   **thousandths; 0.004**

2. 1.8<u>2</u>   **hundredths; 0.02**

3. 3.8<u>7</u>   **hundredths; 0.07**

4. 4.<u>9</u>5   **tenths; 0.9**

5. 12.93<u>1</u>   **thousandths; 0.001**

6. 135.<u>4</u>82   **tenths; 0.4**

Write each number in standard form.

7. 17 and 134 thousandths   **17.134**

8. 263 and 4 hundredths   **263.04**

9. 10 + 0.04 + 0.002   **10.042**

10. 4 + 0.9 + 0.01 + 0.006   **4.916**

Write each number in expanded form.

11. 174.273   **100 + 70 + 4 + 0.2 + 0.07 + 0.003**

12. 30.024   **30 + 0.02 + 0.004**

13. 209.106   **200 + 9 + 0.1 + 0.006**

14. 44.815   **40 + 4 + 0.8 + 0.01 + 0.005**

Spiral Review

Write each fraction as a decimal. (Lesson 1–4)

15. $\frac{3}{10}$ **0.3**

16. $\frac{1}{10}$ **0.1**

17. $\frac{67}{100}$ **0.67**

18. $\frac{7}{100}$ **0.07**

19. $\frac{413}{1,000}$ **0.413**

20. $\frac{5}{1,000}$ **0.005**

Grade 5   30   Chapter 1

Answers

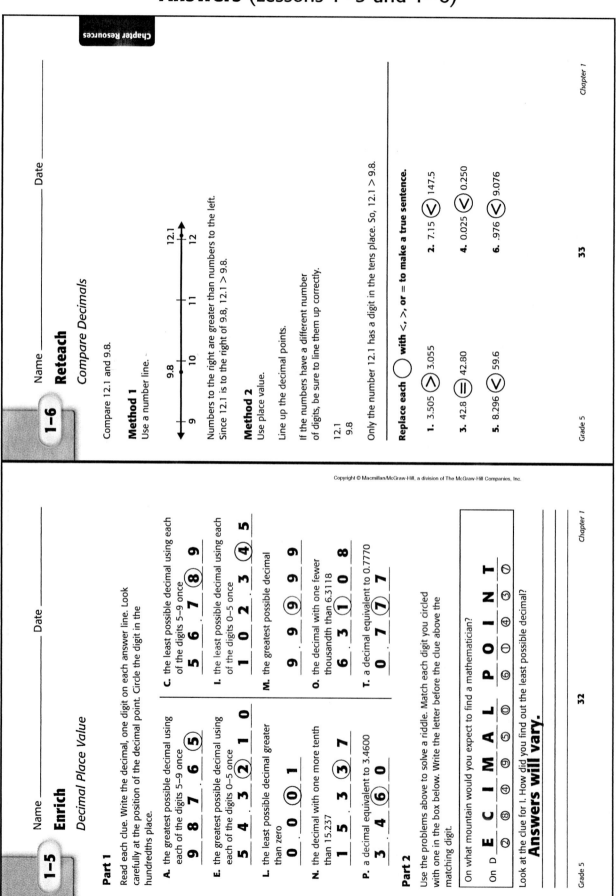

1-6 Reteach — Compare Decimals

Name _____ Date _____

Compare 12.1 and 9.8.

Method 1
Use a number line.

[number line from 9 to 12, with 9.8 and 12.1 marked]

Numbers to the right are greater than numbers to the left.
Since 12.1 is to the right of 9.8, 12.1 > 9.8.

Method 2
Use place value.

Line up the decimal points.

If the numbers have a different number of digits, be sure to line them up correctly.

12.1
9.8

Only the number 12.1 has a digit in the tens place. So, 12.1 > 9.8.

Replace each ◯ with <, >, or = to make a true sentence.

1. 3.505 ⟨>⟩ 3.055   2. 7.15 ⟨<⟩ 147.5

3. 42.8 ⟨=⟩ 42.80   4. 0.025 ⟨<⟩ 0.250

5. 8.296 ⟨<⟩ 59.6   6. .976 ⟨<⟩ 9.076

Grade 5   **33**   *Chapter 1*

1-5 Enrich — Decimal Place Value

Name _____ Date _____

Part 1

Read each clue. Write the decimal, one digit on each answer line. Look carefully at the position of the decimal point. Circle the digit in the hundredths place.

A. the greatest possible decimal using each of the digits 5–9 once
9 8 7 . 6 ⑤

E. the greatest possible decimal using each of the digits 0–5 once
5 4 3 . ② 1 0

L. the least possible decimal greater than zero
0 . 0 ⓪ 1

N. the decimal with one more tenth than 15.237
1 5 . 3 ③ 7

P. a decimal equivalent to 3.4600
3 . 4 ⑥ 0

C. the least possible decimal using each of the digits 5–9 once
5 6 7 . ⑧ 9

I. the least possible decimal using each of the digits 0–5 once
1 0 2 . 3 ④ 5

M. the greatest possible decimal
9 . 9 ⑨ 9 9

O. the decimal with one fewer thousandth than 6.3118
6 . 3 ① 0 8

T. a decimal equivalent to 0.7770
0 . 7 ⑦ 7

Part 2

Use the problems above to solve a riddle. Match each digit you circled with one in the box below. Write the letter before the clue above the matching digit.

On what mountain would you expect to find a mathematician?

On D E C I M A L   P O I N T
    ⓪ ⑧ ⑧ ④ ⑨ ⑥ ⑤   ⑥ ① ④ ③ ①

Look at the clue for I. How did you find out the least possible decimal?
Answers will vary.

Grade 5   **32**   *Chapter 1*

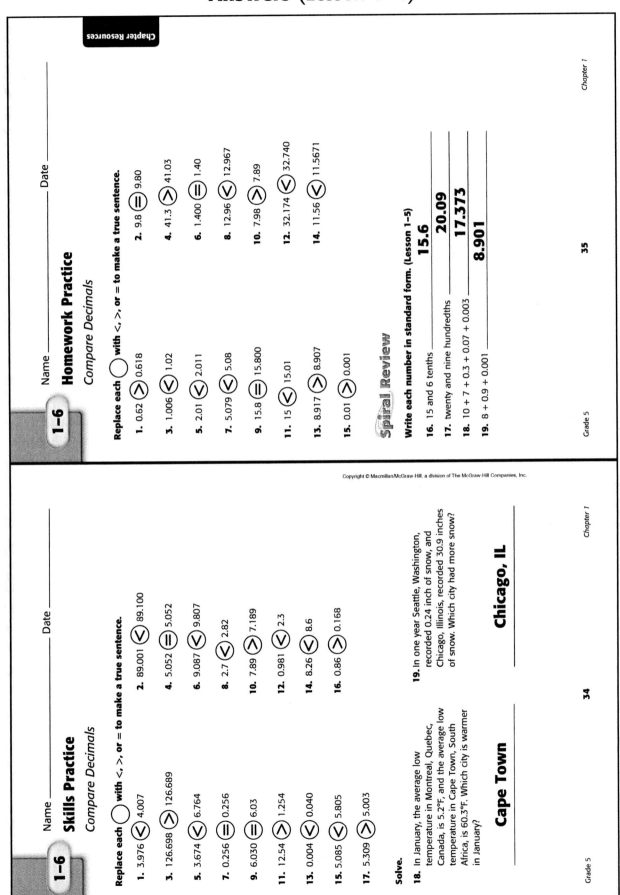

1-6 Homework Practice
Compare Decimals

Name _____ Date _____

Replace each ◯ with <, >, or = to make a true sentence.

1. 0.62 ⟩ 0.618
2. 9.8 = 9.80
3. 1.006 ⟨ 1.02
4. 41.3 ⟩ 41.03
5. 2.01 ⟨ 2.011
6. 1.400 = 1.40
7. 5.079 ⟨ 5.08
8. 12.96 ⟨ 12.967
9. 15.8 = 15.800
10. 7.98 ⟩ 7.89
11. 15 ⟨ 15.01
12. 32.174 ⟨ 32.740
13. 8.917 ⟩ 8.907
14. 11.56 ⟨ 11.5671
15. 0.01 ⟩ 0.001

Spiral Review
Write each number in standard form. (Lesson 1–5)

16. 15 and 6 tenths **15.6**
17. twenty and nine hundredths **20.09**
18. 10 + 7 + 0.3 + 0.07 + 0.003 **17.373**
19. 8 + 0.9 + 0.001 **8.901**

1-6 Skills Practice
Compare Decimals

Name _____ Date _____

Replace each ◯ with <, >, or = to make a true sentence.

1. 3.976 ⟨ 4.007
2. 89.001 ⟨ 89.100
3. 126.698 ⟩ 126.689
4. 5.052 = 5.052
5. 3.674 ⟨ 6.764
6. 9.087 ⟨ 9.807
7. 0.256 = 0.256
8. 2.7 ⟨ 2.82
9. 6.030 = 6.03
10. 7.89 ⟩ 7.189
11. 12.54 ⟩ 1.254
12. 0.981 ⟨ 2.3
13. 0.004 ⟨ 0.040
14. 8.26 ⟨ 8.6
15. 5.085 ⟨ 5.805
16. 0.86 ⟩ 0.168

Solve.

18. In January, the average low temperature in Montreal, Quebec, Canada, is 5.2°F, and the average low temperature in Cape Town, South Africa, is 60.3°F. Which city is warmer in January?

Cape Town

19. In one year Seattle, Washington, recorded 0.24 inch of snow, and Chicago, Illinois, recorded 30.9 inches of snow. Which city had more snow?

Chicago, IL

Answers

Answers (Lesson 1–6)

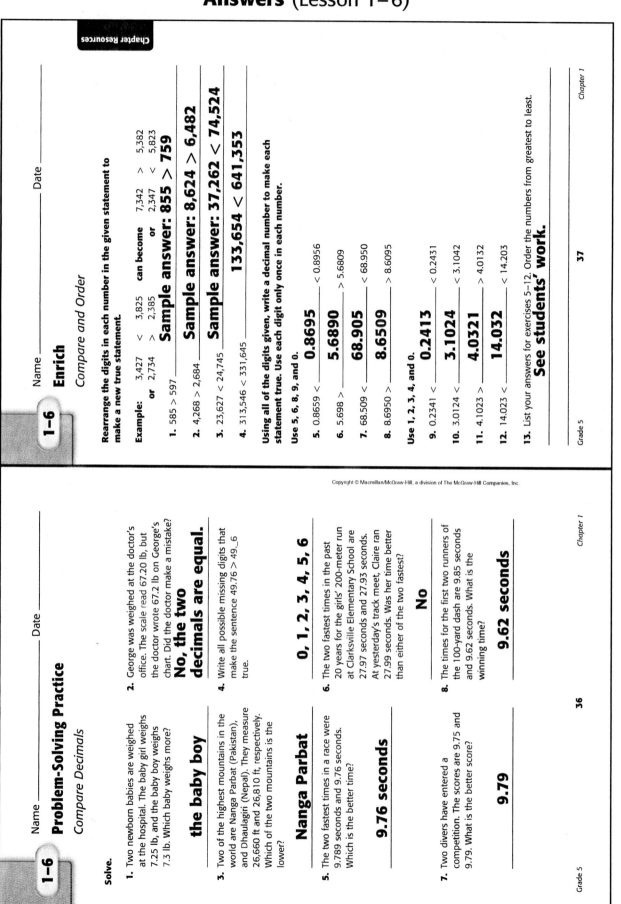

1-6

Name _____ Date _____

Enrich

Compare and Order

Rearrange the digits in each number in the given statement to make a new true statement.

Example: 3,427 < 3,825   **can become**   7,342 > 5,382
      or   2,734 > 2,385   **or**   2,347 < 5,823

1. 585 > 597   **Sample answer: 855 > 759**

2. 4,268 > 2,684   **Sample answer: 8,624 > 6,482**

3. 23,627 < 24,745   **Sample answer: 37,262 < 74,524**

4. 313,546 < 331,645   **133,654 < 641,353**

Using all of the digits given, write a decimal number to make each statement true. Use each digit only once in each number.

Use 5, 6, 8, 9, and 0.

5. 0.8659 < __ **0.8695** __ < 0.8956

6. 5.698 > __ **5.6890** __ > 5.6809

7. 68.509 < __ **68.905** __ < 68.950

8. 8.6950 > __ **8.6509** __ > 8.6095

Use 1, 2, 3, 4, and 0.

9. 0.2341 < __ **0.2413** __ < 0.2431

10. 3.0124 < __ **3.1024** __ < 3.1042

11. 4.1023 > __ **4.0321** __ > 4.0132

12. 14.023 < __ **14.032** __ < 14.203

13. List your answers for exercises 5–12. Order the numbers from greatest to least. **See students' work.**

Grade 5   37   Chapter 1

1-6

Name _____ Date _____

Problem-Solving Practice

Compare Decimals

Solve.

1. Two newborn babies are weighed at the hospital. The baby girl weighs 7.25 lb, and the baby boy weighs 7.3 lb. Which baby weighs more?

   the baby boy

2. George was weighed at the doctor's office. The scale read 67.20 lb, but the doctor wrote 67.2 lb on George's chart. Did the doctor make a mistake? **No, the two decimals are equal.**

3. Two of the highest mountains in the world are Nanga Parbat (Pakistan), and Dhaulagiri (Nepal). They measure 26,660 ft and 26,810 ft, respectively. Which of the two mountains is the lower?

   Nanga Parbat

4. Write all possible missing digits that make the sentence 49.76 > 49.__6 true.

   0, 1, 2, 3, 4, 5, 6

5. The two fastest times in a race were 9.789 seconds and 9.76 seconds. Which is the better time?

   9.76 seconds

6. The two fastest times in the past 20 years for the girls' 200-meter run at Clarksville Elementary School are 27.97 seconds and 27.93 seconds. At yesterday's track meet, Claire ran 27.99 seconds. Was her time better than either of the two fastest?

   No

7. Two divers have entered a competition. The scores are 9.75 and 9.79. What is the better score?

   9.79

8. The times for the first two runners of the 100-yard dash are 9.85 seconds and 9.62 seconds. What is the winning time?

   9.62 seconds

Grade 5   36   Chapter 1

Answers (Lesson 1–7)

1-7 Reteach

Name _____ Date _____

Order Whole Numbers and Decimals

You can write numbers in expanded form to compare them.

- Compare 43,058 and 48,503.
  Write the numbers in expanded form.

  $43,058 = 40,000 + 3,000 + 50 + 8$

  $48,503 = 40,000 + 8,000 + 500 + 3$

  Compare the numbers, starting with the greatest place.

  $\boxed{40,000 = 40,000}\quad 3,000, < 8,000$

  So, $43,058, < 48,503.$

- Compare 12.106 and 9.837.
  If the numbers have a different number of digits, be sure to line them up correctly.

  $12.106 = 10 + 2 + 0.1 + \quad 0.006$
  $9.837 = \qquad 9 + 0.8 + 0.03 + 0.007$

  Only the number 12.106 has a digit in the tens place. So, $12.106 > 9.837.$

Write the numbers in expanded form. Replace each ◯ with >, < or = to compare each pair of numbers.

1. $3,505 = \underline{3,000 + 500 + 5}$

   $3,055 = \underline{3,000 + 50 + 5}$

   $3,505 \; \text{>} \; 3,055$

2. $7.15 = \underline{7 + 0.1 + 0.05}$

   $17.5 = \underline{10 + 7 + 0.5}$

   $7.15 \; \text{<} \; 17.5$

3. $42.8 = \underline{40 + 2 + 0.8}$

   $42.80 = \underline{40 + 2 + 0.8}$

   $42.8 \; \text{=} \; 42.80$

4. $0.025 = \underline{0.02 + 0.005}$

   $0.250 = \underline{0.2 + 0.05}$

   $0.025 \; \text{<} \; 0.250$

5. $8,296 = \underline{8,000 + 200 + 90 + 6}$

   $596 = \underline{500 + 90 + 6}$

   $8,296 \; \text{>} \; 596$

6. $4,000,976 = \underline{4,000,000 + 900 + 70 + 6}$

   $4,009,076 = \underline{4,000,000 + 9000 + 70 + 6}$

   $4,000,976 \; \text{<} \; 4,009,076$

1-7 Skills Practice

Name _____ Date _____

Order Whole Numbers and Decimals

Replace each ◯ with >, <, or = to compare each pair of numbers.

1. $3,976 \; \text{<} \; 4,007$

2. $89,001 \; \text{<} \; 89,100$

3. $126,698 \; \text{>} \; 126,689$

4. $1,455,052 \; \text{>} \; 145,052$

5. $19,463,674 \; \text{<} \; 29,436,764$

6. $4,303,259,087 \; \text{>} \; 4,033,259,807$

7. $2.7 \; \text{<} \; 2.82$

8. $6.030 \; \text{=} \; 6.03$

9. $7.89 \; \text{>} \; 7.189$

10. $12.54 \; \text{>} \; 1.254$

11. $0.981 \; \text{<} \; 2.3$

12. $0.004 \; \text{<} \; 0.040$

Order each set of numbers from least to greatest.

13. 17,639; 3,828; 45,947   **3,828; 17,639; 45,947**

14. 890,409; 890,904; 809,904   **809,904; 890,409; 890,904**

15. 0.186; 0.1; 0.86; 0.168   **0.1; 0.168; 0.186; 0.86**

16. 5.309; 5.003; 0.53; 0.9   **0.53; 0.9; 5.003; 5.309**

Solve.

17. In City A, the average low temperature is 7.4°F, and the average low temperature in City B is 54.1°F. Which city is warmer?

   City B

18. In one year Seattle recorded 0.24 inch of snow, Chicago recorded 30.9 inches of snow, and Birmingham recorded 1 inch of snow. Write these amounts in order from least to greatest.

   0.24 in., 1 in., 30.9 in.

Answers

Answers (Lesson 1–7)

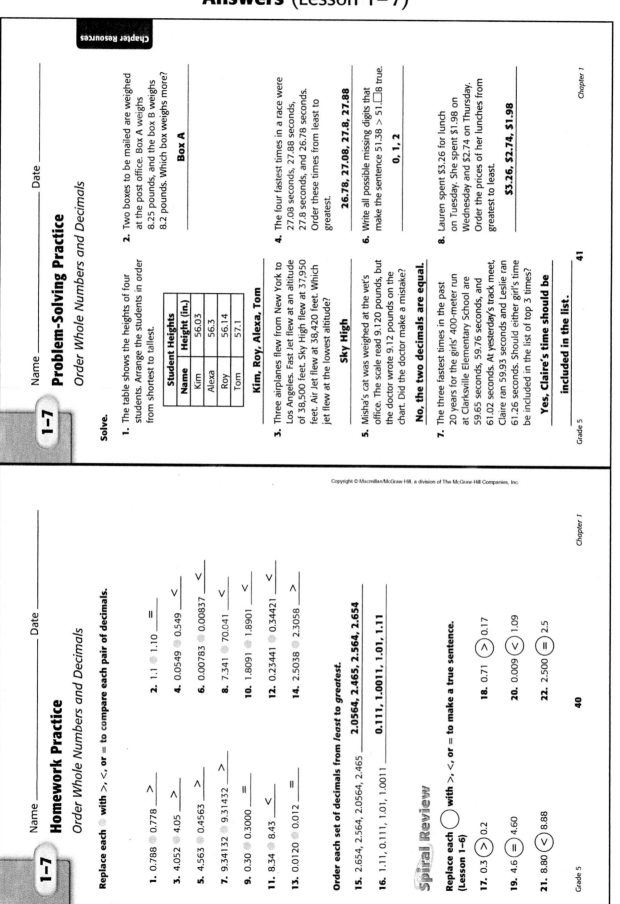

Name _____ Date _____

1-7 Homework Practice

Order Whole Numbers and Decimals

Replace each ● with >, <, or = to compare each pair of decimals.

1. 0.788 ● 0.778 **>**

2. 1.1 ● 1.10 **=**

3. 4.052 ● 4.05 **>**

4. 0.0549 ● 0.549 **<**

5. 4.563 ● 0.4563 **>**

6. 0.00783 ● 0.00837 **<**

7. 9.34132 ● 9.31432 **>**

8. 7.341 ● 70.041 **<**

9. 0.30 ● 0.3000 **=**

10. 1.8091 ● 1.8901 **<**

11. 8.34 ● 8.43 **<**

12. 0.23441 ● 0.34421 **<**

13. 0.0120 ● 0.012 **=**

14. 2.5038 ● 2.3058 **>**

Order each set of decimals from *least to greatest.*

15. 2.654, 2.564, 2.0564, 2.465   **2.0564, 2.465, 2.564, 2.654**

16. 1.11, 0.111, 1.01, 1.0011   **0.111, 1.0011, 1.01, 1.11**

Spiral Review

Replace each ◯ with >, <, or = to make a true sentence.
(Lesson 1–6)

17. 0.3 (>) 0.2

18. 0.71 (>) 0.17

19. 4.6 (=) 4.60

20. 0.009 (<) 1.09

21. 8.80 (<) 8.88

22. 2.500 (=) 2.5

Grade 5   40   *Chapter 1*

Name _____ Date _____

1-7 Problem-Solving Practice

Order Whole Numbers and Decimals

Solve.

1. The table shows the heights of four students. Arrange the students in order from shortest to tallest.

   Student Heights

Name	Height (in.)
Kim	56.03
Alexa	56.3
Roy	56.14
Tom	57.1

   Kim, Roy, Alexa, Tom

2. Two boxes to be mailed are weighed at the post office. Box A weighs 8.25 pounds, and the box B weighs 8.2 pounds. Which box weighs more?

   Box A

3. Three airplanes flew from New York to Los Angeles. Fast Jet flew at an altitude of 38,500 feet. Sky High flew at 37,950 feet. Air Jet flew at 38,420 feet. Which jet flew at the lowest altitude?

   Sky High

4. The four fastest times in a race were 27.08 seconds, 27.88 seconds, 27.8 seconds, and 26.78 seconds. Order these times from least to greatest.

   26.78, 27.08, 27.8, 27.88

5. Misha's cat was weighed at the vet's office. The scale read 9.120 pounds, but the doctor wrote 9.12 pounds on the chart. Did the doctor make a mistake?

   No, the two decimals are equal.

6. Write all possible missing digits that make the sentence 51.38 > 51.☐8 true.

   0, 1, 2

7. The three fastest times in the past 20 years for the girls' 400-meter run at Clarksville Elementary School are 59.65 seconds, 59.76 seconds, and 61.02 seconds. At yesterday's track meet, Claire ran 59.93 seconds and Leslie ran 61.26 seconds. Should either girl's time be included in the list of top 3 times?

   Yes, Claire's time should be included in the list.

8. Lauren spent $3.26 for lunch on Tuesday. She spent $1.98 on Wednesday and $2.74 on Thursday. Order the prices of her lunches from greatest to least.

   $3.26, $2.74, $1.98

Grade 5   41   *Chapter 1*

Name _____ Date _____

1-7 Enrich

Hurdling the Competition

Use the data from the table to solve.

Men's Olympic 400-Meter Hurdles		
Year	**Gold Medal Winner**	**Time (in seconds)**
1980	Volker Beck	48.70
1984	Edwin Moses	47.75
1988	Andre Phillips	47.19
1992	Kevin Young	46.78
1996	Derrick Adkins	47.54
2000	Angelo Taylor	47.50
2004	Felix Sanchez	47.63

1. List Andre Phillips, Kevin Young, and Derrick Adkins from fastest to slowest.
   Kevin Young, Andre Phillips, Derrick Adkins

2. Which gold medal winner has the fastest time in the 400-meter hurdles?
   Kevin Young

3. How much less time did it take Angelo Taylor in 2000 than it took Derrick Adkins in 1996?
   0.04 seconds

4. Which athlete has the slowest time?
   Volker Beck

5. In 1976, Edwin Moses won a gold medal in the 400-meter hurdles with a time of 47.64 seconds. How much faster was his time in 1976 than in 1984?
   0.11 seconds

6. What are the athlete's names in order from slowest time to fastest time?
   Volker Beck, Edwin Moses, Felix Sanchez, Derrick Adkins, Angelo Taylor, Andre Phillips, Kevin Young

7. Who had a time 0.25 second faster than Edwin Moses had in 1984?
   Angelo Taylor

8. In what year did an athlete have a gold-medal-winning time of 0.19 second more than 47 seconds?
   1988

9. What is the difference between the fastest time and the slowest time?
   1.92 seconds

10. How many years after Andre Phillips won a gold medal did Felix Sanchez win a gold medal?
    16 years

Name _____ Date _____

1-8 Reteach

Problem-Solving Strategy: Guess and Check

Guess and Check

During summer vacation, Sanjay writes letters and postcards to his friends at home. A letter costs $0.41 to mail, and a postcard costs $0.21 to mail. Sanjay writes to 8 friends and spends $2.08. How many letters and postcards does he send?

Step 1 Understand	**Be sure you understand the problem.** Read carefully. Identify what you need to do. What facts do you know? • A letter costs **$0.41** and a postcard costs **$0.21** to mail. • Sanjay writes to **8 friends** • He spends **$2.08** What do you need to find? • The number of **letters and postcards he sent**
Step 2 Plan	**Make a plan.** Choose a strategy. You can solve the problem by making a guess. Then check the guess. If it is not the correct answer, adjust the guess and check again until you find the correct answer. • Use Logical Reasoning • Draw a Diagram • Make a Graph • Make a Table or List • Find a Pattern • Guess and Check

Answers (Lesson 1–8)

1-8

Name _____ Date _____

Reteach

Problem-Solving Strategy: Guess and Check

Step 3 Solve	**Follow your plan.**
	Make a guess about the number of letters and the number of postcards. Suppose you guess 4 letters and 4 postcards.

Answers may vary. Students should guess and check until they find 2 letters ($0.82) and 6 postcards ($1.26). The total cost is $2.08.

Check the amounts for the guess.

Letters: $4 \times \$0.41 = \$1.64$
Postcards: $4 \times 21¢ = \$0.84$
Total Cost: $\$1.64 + \$0.84 = \$2.48$

Does the guess check with the total that Sanjay spent? **No.**

Should you adjust the number of letters up or down? Explain.
Adjust the number of letters down because the total is too much.

Adjust your guess. Check your guess. **Answers may vary.**
Did the guess check? **Answers may vary.**
If your guess did not check, adjust it again.

How many letters does Sanjay send? **2 letters**
How many postcards does Sanjay send? **6 postcards**

Step 4 Check	**Look back. Did you answer the question?** Is the solution reasonable? Reread the problem.

Have you answered the question? **Yes.**

How can you check your answer? **Answers may vary.**
Possible answer: check the total cost for the letters and postcards.

Practice

1. Nelson has 7 coins. All the coins are dimes and quarters. He has a total of $1.15. How many dimes and how many quarters does he have?

3 quarters and 4 dimes

2. The library charges $0.75 a day for overdue videos and $0.12 a day for overdue books. Emily returns a video and a book and pays a total of $3.48 in late fees. How many days late were her items?

4 days

Grade 5 · · · 44 · · · *Chapter 1*

Name _____ Date _____

1-8

Skills Practice

Problem-Solving Strategy: Guess and Check

Use the guess and check strategy to solve.

1. The Bactrian camel has two humps and the Dromedary camel has one hump. In a group of 15 camels, the total number of humps is 21. How many camels of each type are there?

9 Dromedary and 6 Bactrian

2. The circus orders bicycles and unicycles for a new act. It orders a total of 12 cycles. The cycles have 16 tires altogether. How many bicycles and unicycles did the circus order?

8 unicycles and 4 bicycles

3. Anja buys a magazine and a pizza. She spends $8.10. The magazine costs $2.40 less than the pizza. How much does the pizza cost?

$5.25

4. A letter to Europe from the United States costs $0.80 to mail. A letter mailed within the United States costs $0.41. Nancy mails 5 letters for $2.83, some to Europe and some to the United States. How many letters did she send to Europe?

2 letters

5. Warren spent $8.50 at the store. He spent $2.40 on paper, $0.88 on pencils, and $2.65 on markers. He spent the rest on a notebook. How much did the notebook cost?

$2.57

6. Ms. Baxter takes a group of 8 children to a concert. Tickets for children 12 years and older cost $3.50. Tickets for children under 12 cost $2.25. She spends a total of $21.75 on tickets for the children. How many children are 12 and older?

3 children

Grade 5 · · · 45 · · · *Chapter 1*

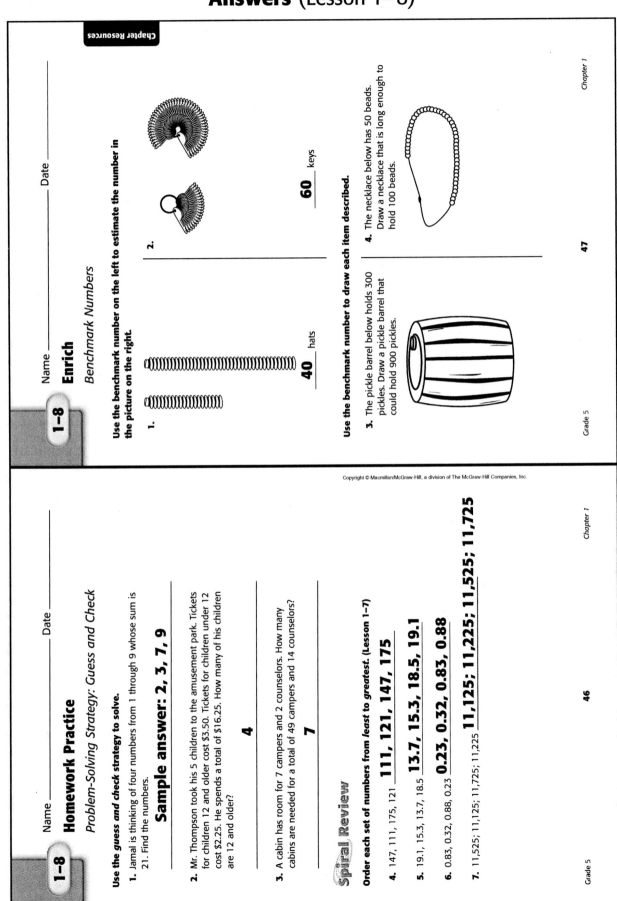

Chapter Resources

1-8

Name _____ Date _____

Enrich

Benchmark Numbers

Use the benchmark number on the left to estimate the number in the picture on the right.

1.

40 hats

2.

60 keys

Use the benchmark number to draw each item described.

3. The pickle barrel below holds 300 pickles. Draw a pickle barrel that could hold 900 pickles.

4. The necklace below has 50 beads. Draw a necklace that is long enough to hold 100 beads.

Grade 5 — 47 — Chapter 1

1-8

Name _____ Date _____

Homework Practice

Problem-Solving Strategy: Guess and Check

Use the *guess and check* strategy to solve.

1. Jamal is thinking of four numbers from 1 through 9 whose sum is 21. Find the numbers.

Sample answer: 2, 3, 7, 9

2. Mr. Thompson took his 5 children to the amusement park. Tickets for children 12 and older cost $3.50. Tickets for children under 12 cost $2.25. He spends a total of $16.25. How many of his children are 12 and older?

4

3. A cabin has room for 7 campers and 2 counselors. How many cabins are needed for a total of 49 campers and 14 counselors?

7

Spiral Review

Order each set of numbers from *least* to *greatest*. (Lesson 1–7)

4. 147, 111, 175, 121   **111, 121, 147, 175**

5. 19.1, 15.3, 13.7, 18.5   **13.7, 15.3, 18.5, 19.1**

6. 0.83, 0.32, 0.88, 0.23   **0.23, 0.32, 0.83, 0.88**

7. 11,525; 11,125; 11,725; 11,225   **11,125; 11,225; 11,525; 11,725**

Grade 5 — 46 — Chapter 1

Answers

Answers (Vocabulary Test and Oral Assessment)

Vocabulary Test side

Name _____ Date _____

Vocabulary Test

1

Use the word list at the bottom of the page to complete each of the following statements.

Decimals that have the same value are __**equivalent decimals**__ .

__**place value**__ is a system for writing numbers. In this system, the position of a digit determines its value.

A __**fraction**__ is a number that names part of a whole or group.

The usual or common way to write a number is called __**standard form**__ .

A __**whole number**__ is any one of the numbers 0, 1, 2, 3…

The way of writing a number as the sum of the *values* of its digits is called __**expanded form**__ .

A __**decimal**__ is a number with one or more digits to the right of the decimal point.

Word List

decimal	place value	
equivalent decimals	standard form	
expanded form	whole number	
fraction		

Assessment

Oral Assessment side

Name _____ Date _____

Oral Assessment

1

Read each question aloud to the student. Then write the student's answers on the lines below the question.

Write the number 879,456,231 where the student can see it.

1. What is the value of the 5 in this number?

50,000

2. What is the place value of the 8 in this number?

hundred millions

3. Which number is in the ten millions place?

7

4. Tell how you got your answer.

I used place value.

Answers (Oral Assessment)

Name _____ Date _____

1

Oral Assessment   *(continued)*

Write the number 12.637 where the student can see it.

5. What is the value of the 7 in this number?

0.007

6. What is the place value of the 3 in this number?

hundredths

7. To order a set of numbers from greatest to least, what would you do?

I would look to see which number has the greatest number in the highest place value.

Assessment

Answers

Chapter 1 Assessment Answer Key

Inventory Placement Test
Page 48

Page 49

1. **83,308; 83,083; 38,830; 38,803**

2. **$338.84**

3. **4 dimes**

4. $y = x - 2$

5. **August**

6. **99**

7. **24 and 25**

8. **13**

9. **32**

10. **36,159**

11. **121 R3**

12. **25**

13. **equilateral and acute**

14. **12 ft**

15. **(4, 7)**

16. **5**

17. $5\frac{1}{2}$

18. **0.07**

19. **39.27**

20. $\frac{1}{4}$

1. **six**

2. **eighteen**

3. **thirty-four**

4. **forty-one**

5. **one hundred fifty**

6. **two hundred seventy-one**

7. **1**

8. **13**

9. **3**

10. **8**

11. **6**

12. **12**

13. **5 < 9**

14. **41 > 12**

15. **92 = 92**

16. **231 > 230**

17. **14 < 16**

Chapter 1 Assessment Answer Key

Chapter Pretest
Page 52

1. _____ tens _____
2. _____ ten thousands _____
3. _____ thousands _____
4. _____ hundred millions _____

5. _____ < _____
6. _____ > _____
7. _____ = _____
8. _____ < _____

9. _____ 0.683 _____
10. _____ 0.7 _____
11. _____ 0.06 _____
12. _____ 0.91 _____

Quiz 1
Page 53

1. _____ 3,939,402 _____
2. _____ 13,304,012 _____
3. _____ 19,560 _____

4. _____ two thousand, eight hundred ninety seven _____
5. _____ six billion, seven hundred thousand, two _____

6. _____ = _____
7. _____ > _____
8. _____ < _____
9. _____ > _____

10. _____ $25 _____

11. _____ Rachel _____

Quiz 2
Page 54

1. _____ 0.3 _____
2. _____ 0.673 _____
3. _____ 0.09 _____

4. _____ tenths; 0.90 _____
5. _____ thousandths; 0.002 _____

6. _____ 40.09 _____
7. _____ 7.018 _____

8. _____ < _____
9. _____ > _____
10. _____ = _____
11. _____ 2 + 0.7 + 0.06 _____

Chapter 1 Assessment Answer Key

Quiz 3
Page 55

1. 432, 439, 598, 801
2. 2.09, 2.45, 2.49, 2.94
3. 61, 61.008, 61.01, 62.47, 62.8
4. 4.99, 5.009, 5.08, 5.20
5. 0.001, 0.010, 0.10, 1.000, 1.10
6. 3.14, 31.4, 34.824, 34.842, 348.24

7. 1 duck and 3 dogs

8. 4 dogs and 3 birds

Mid-Chapter Test
Page 56

1. A
2. H
3. B
4. J
5. B
6. H
7. B
8. ten billions
9. 87 million, 20

10. 718,038
11. 39,068,808

Chapter Test, Form 1
Page 62

1. B
2. H
3. B
4. F
5. A
6. J
7. B
8. G
9. D

(continued on the next page)

Chapter 1 Assessment Answer Key

Chapter Test, Form 1
(*continued*)
Page 63

10. **F**

11. **B**

12. **H**

13. **D**

14. **H**

15. **B**

16. **G**

Chapter Test, Form 2A
Page 64

1. **C**

2. **H**

3. **B**

4. **F**

5. **A**

6. **J**

7. **B**

8. **G**

9. **D**

10. **F**

Page 65

11. **C**

12. **H**

13. **D**

14. **H**

15. **B**

16. **G**

Answers

Chapter 1 Assessment Answer Key

Chapter Test, Form 2B
Page 66

1. __**B**__

2. __**H**__

3. __**B**__

4. __**F**__

5. __**A**__

6. __**H**__

7. __**B**__

8. __**G**__

9. __**C**__

10. __**F**__

Page 67

11. __**C**__

12. __**H**__

13. __**C**__

14. __**H**__

15. __**B**__

16. __**G**__

Chapter Test, Form 2C
Page 68

1. __**800,000**__

2. __**0.005**__

3. __**ten millions**__

4. __**thousandths**__

5. __**500,000 + 60,000 + 700 + 30 + 2**__

6. __**eight hundred twenty-one million**__

7. __**>**__

8. __**>**__

9. __**=**__

10. __**1 million, 584 thousand, 296**__

(continued on the next page)

Chapter 1 Assessment Answer Key

11. _____ **0.3** _____

12. _____ **0.016** _____

13. _____ **0.871** _____

14. _____ $\dfrac{7}{10}$ _____

15. _____ $\dfrac{67}{100}$ _____

16. _____ $\dfrac{93}{1,000}$ _____

17. _____ **0.5** _____

18. _____ **0.106, 0.160, 0.3, 0.302, 0.32** _____

19. _____ **8,762,176; 9,345,287; 92,239,939; 1,012,224,981** _____

1. _____ **800,000** _____

2. _____ **0.005** _____

3. _____ **ten millions** _____

4. _____ **thousandths** _____

5. _____ **500,000 + 60,000 + 700 + 30 + 2** _____

6. _____ **93 million** _____

7. _____ **>** _____

8. _____ **>** _____

9. _____ **=** _____

10. _____ **1 million, 584 thousand, 296** _____

11. _____ **0.3** _____

12. _____ **0.016** _____

13. _____ **0.871** _____

14. _____ $\dfrac{7}{10}$ _____

15. _____ $\dfrac{67}{100}$ _____

16. _____ $\dfrac{93}{1,000}$ _____

17. _____ **0.5** _____

18. _____ **0.106, 0.160, 0.3, 0.302, 0.32** _____

19. _____ **8,762,176; 9,345,287; 92,239,939; 1,012,224,981** _____

Answers

Chapter 1 Assessment Answer Key

Chapter Test, Form 3
Page 72

1. _____ **800,000** _____

2. _____ **0.005** _____

3. _____ **ten millions** _____

4. _____ **thousandths** _____

5. _____ **500,000 + 60,000 + 700 + 30 + 2** _____

6. _____ **eight hundred twenty-one million** _____

7. _____ **>** _____

8. _____ **>** _____

9. _____ **=** _____

10. **1 million, 584 thousand, 296**

Page 73

11. _____ **0.3** _____

12. _____ **0.016** _____

13. _____ **0.871** _____

14. _____ $\dfrac{7}{10}$ _____

15. _____ $\dfrac{67}{100}$ _____

16. _____ $\dfrac{93}{1,000}$ _____

17. _____ **0.5** _____

18. _____ **0.106, 0.160, 0.3, 0.302, 0.32** _____

19. _____ **8,762,176; 9,345,287; 92,239,939; 1,012,224,981** _____

Chapter 1 Assessment Answer Key

Page 74, Chapter Extended-Response Test
Scoring Rubric

Level	Specific Criteria
4	The student demonstrates a **thorough understanding** of the mathematics concepts and/or procedures embodied in the task. The student has responded correctly to the task, used mathematically sound procedures, and provided clear and complete explanations and interpretations. The response may contain minor flaws that do not detract from the demonstration of a thorough understanding.
3	The student demonstrates an **understanding** of the mathematics concepts and/or procedures embodied in the task. The student's response to the task is essentially correct with the mathematical procedures used and the explanations and interpretations provided demonstrating an essential but less than thorough understanding. The response may contain minor errors that reflect inattentive execution of the mathematical procedures or indications of some misunderstanding of the underlying mathematics concepts and/or procedures.
2	The student has demonstrated only a **partial understanding** of the mathematics concepts and/or procedures embodied in the task. Although the student may have used the correct approach to obtaining a solution or may have provided a correct solution, the student's work lacks an essential understanding of the underlying mathematical concepts. The response contains errors related to misunderstanding important aspects of the task, misuse of mathematical procedures, or faulty interpretations of results.
1	The student has demonstrated a **very limited understanding** of the mathematics concepts and/or procedures embodied in the task. The student's response to the task is incomplete and exhibits many flaws. Although the student has addressed some of the conditions of the task, the student reached an inadequate conclusion and/or provided reasoning that was faulty or incomplete. The response exhibits many errors or may be incomplete.
0	The student has provided a **completely incorrect** solution or uninterpretable response, or no response at all.

Answers

Chapter 1 Assessment Answer Key

Page 74, Chapter Extended-Response Test
Sample Answers

In addition to the scoring rubric found on page A36, the following sample answers may be used as guidance in evaluating open-ended assessment items.

1. Understand. Be sure you understand the problem. What do you know? What do you need to find out. Plan: Plan a strategy for solving the problem. Solve: Use your plan to solve the problem. Check: Does the answer make sense?

2. First line up the numbers. Then compare the digits in the greatest place. Then compare the digits in the next place.

3. Find the value of each digit and add them together. $5 + 0.3 + 0.01 + 0.002$.

Chapter 1 Assessment Answer Key

Cumulative Test Practice Chapter 1

Page 75	Page 76	Page 77
	3. **B**	8. **J**
		9. **A**
	4. **F**	
	5. **D**	10. **F**
	6. **J**	11. 25.44
		12. 3,000,000 + 400,000 + 60,000 + 300 + 1
1. **C**	7. **B**	
2. **G**		13. $0.05

Answers

AMAZEing ART™

Wonders of
the Ancient World

CHRISTOPHER BERG

Quill
A HarperResource Book
An Imprint of HarperCollins*Publishers*

FIRST EDITION

DESIGNED BY DEBORAH KERNER / DANCING BEARS DESIGN

Printed on acid-free paper

Library of Congress Cataloging-in-Publication Data

Berg, Christopher, 1966-

Amazeing art: wonders of the ancient world/Christopher Berg.—1st ed.

p. cm.

Includes bibliographical references.

ISBN 0-06-095674-7 (trade paper)

1. Civilization, Ancient—Pictorial works. 2. Antiquities—Pictorial works. 3. Historic sites—Pictorial works.

4. Seven Wonders of the World—Pictorial works. 5. Maze puzzles. 6. Civilization, Ancient. 7. Antiquities.

8. Historic sites. 9. Seven Wonders of the World. I. Title.

CB311 .B45 2001

930—dc21   2001024497

01 02 03 04 05 ❖/QW 10 9 8 7 6 5 4 3 2 1

CONTENTS

THE MYSTERIES
OF ANTIQUITY

BY DR. JEREMY RUTTER, PROFESSOR OF CLASSICAL ART
AND ARCHAEOLOGY, DARTMOUTH COLLEGE CLASSICS DEPARTMENT

One of the principal challenges archaeologists face is to convey to others that investigating human activities in the distant past is inherently exciting. Christopher Berg has put together a book that has all the ingredients to do this—pictures of ancient monuments in distant lands, engaging historical commentary, and challenging puzzles to be solved. His book seeks to inspire an interest in antiquity—my own goal as a professor—by using several familiar concepts combined in an intriguing new way. Rather than photographs or technical line drawings, his artwork consists of complex, impressionistic labyrinths; and the accompanying text doesn't have the usual dry-as-dust flavor of an encyclopedia entry, but instead is an entertaining and informative mixture of ancient gossip, modern speculation, and hard scientific fact about each of the thirty monuments from the ancient world that he has selected.

A basic but important lesson that archaeologists try to teach their students is to look at an artifact closely, carefully, and from as many different angles as possible in the effort to understand what clues about the past it has to provide. Exercises intended to promote observational skills typically take the form of tedious assignments asking students to describe a coin or pot or fragment of sculpture in the most excruciating detail possible. Now, Christopher Berg has given us a way to learn about an ancient monument through a complex labyrinth that challenges us with its winding passages while it impresses us with the artistry of its design. I give him high marks for his creativity. But more importantly, I doff my educator's hat to him for coming up with a novel way to attract the attention of puzzle-solvers of all ages and backgrounds to a rich assortment of antiquity's more impressive, yet often still mysterious structures.

OZYMANDIAS

I met a traveler from an antique land

Who said: Two vast and trunkless legs of stone

Stand in the desert. . . . Near them, on the sand,

Half sunk, a shattered visage lies, whose frown,

And wrinkled lip, and sneer of cold command,

Tell that its sculptor well those passions read

Which yet survive, stamped on these lifeless things,

The hand that mocked them, and the heart that fed;

And on the pedestal these words appear:

'My name is Ozymandias, king of kings:

Look on my works, ye Mighty, and despair!'

Nothing beside remains. Round the decay

Of that colossal wreck, boundless and bare

The lone and level sands stretch far away.

— PERCY BYSSHE SHELLEY, 1817

THE WONDERS
OF THE ANCIENT WORLD

So Notable a Monument,
Buried in Oblivion

In 1817 Giovanni Belzoni, an adventurous excavator of Egyptian temples and tombs, brought the immense torso of a granite colossus to the British Museum. The torso had been recovered from the Ramesseum, the mortuary temple of Ramesses II in the City of the Dead across the Nile from ancient Thebes, and it caused a sensation in London society. Belzoni, however, had been unable to remove the enormous fragments of a second colossus that had fallen nearby. By all accounts this second colossus had originally stood 60 feet high and had weighed over 900 tons. The tale of its broken foot, lying amid the crumbling ruins of a temple that Ramesses had intended to "last for a million years," inspired one of the museum's visitors, Percy Bysshe Shelley, to pen his famous sonnet "Ozymandias."

Few poems have awakened popular imagination to the vast ebb and flow of history as much as "Ozymandias." It is a sobering image—the colossal statue of a proud king, lying broken amid the boundless desert, with only the testimony of a solitary traveler to bring word of its existence. What unknown tales might lie behind such a colossal ruin? And how did it happen that the great empire that raised it no longer exists?

The Egyptian colossus that inspired Shelley's sonnet, one of the largest freestanding sculptures ever cut from stone, was an architectural and technological marvel of its time. Along with the Roman aqueducts, the Great Wall of China, and the Egyptian pyramids, it is an enduring testament to the control of vast resources and the technical skill of its builders. Such imposing monuments inspire awe and wonder among those who behold them, and even in their time were seen as powerful symbols of the civilizations that raised them. "Will anybody compare the pyramids, or those useless though renowned works of the Greeks, with these aqueducts?" wrote Frontinus, a Roman water commissioner in the first century A.D.

"The ideas that ruins awaken in me are grand. Everything is annihilated, everything perishes, everything passes, there is only the world that remains, only time which endures."

—DENIS DIDEROT, PHILOSOPHER AND ENCYCLOPEDIAST, EIGHTEENTH CENTURY

1

A colossus of Ramessess II lies broken amid the ruins of the Ramesseum.
(Credit: Jeremy Stafford-Deitsch)

He had cause to be proud: The Roman aqueducts, which were engineered to drop in height by only a few feet per mile, brought hundreds of millions of gallons of water into the city of Rome every day—as much water per person as many modern cities can provide.

Today the elegant arched bridges of the aqueducts have fallen into ruin, yet their power to impress us has only increased with age. Like the Great Sphinx, a monument so old that Egyptian pharaohs themselves worshipped it as a god, the ruined aqueducts hint at tales of splendor and of calamity, of distant ages whose memories are only vaguely preserved in the scant material remains that have survived intact into modern times. Over the centuries a sense of mystery has slowly gathered around such ruins, a sense that perhaps somewhere in their past lies an undiscovered and as yet unimaginable tale. Shakespeare wrote of the "undiscover'd country from whose bourn no traveler returns." His words might well be applied to the distant past; we can try to picture it in our mind's eye, but in truth it is utterly beyond our direct comprehension, hidden beyond a horizon no explorer can ever cross. All we can do is collect the few clues we find scattered about—a few stones here, a few written words there—put them together, and marvel at the stories they reveal.

"Truth is always strange," wrote Byron, and the actual tales behind many of the most impressive monuments from antiquity—the reasons they were built, their eventual fates, and the stories and achievements of the men and women who created and lived with them—are just as captivating as Shelley's flights of poetic fancy in "Ozymandias." On top of the Ziggurat of Marduk at Babylon, a 300-foot-tall multicolored stepped pyramid that was almost certainly the inspiration behind the biblical Tower of Babel, lay nothing more than an opulent bedchamber. This was occupied at night by only one woman, chosen from among all the women of Babylon to be the companion of the god Marduk, who was believed to dwell atop the ziggurat. Upon the summits of Mayan pyramids, which were both temples and tombs, Mayan lords communicated via narrow stone tubes with their ancestors interred in burial chambers far below—while engaging in ritual bloodletting and self-torture. They believed that blood nourished the gods, and that without it, cosmic disorder would result; among other practices they pierced their tongues with stingray spines and passed thorny strings through the holes.

Then there was the Artemesion, a Greek temple that became one of the Wonders of the Ancient World, burned down by a madman whose only purpose was to immortalize his name. Some monuments even contributed to the decline of the civilizations that created them. The Polynesian society on Easter Island, for example, collapsed after the inhabitants felled most of the trees on their island, in part to make the wooden rollers and levers necessary for moving their giant statues.

However startling and varied the stories behind them, such impressive monuments have, over the centuries and millennia, suffered similar fates: They have been toppled by earthquakes, quarried for stone, and despoiled by human hands. Some have been reclaimed by the grasping fingers of the jungle, buried beneath the silt and mud of wandering rivers, or engulfed by desert sands. Yet many of them still endure, visible symbols of man's greatest successes against the inexorable, corroding powers of time and nature.

To the ancients, civilization primarily represented the imposition of order on the chaotic forces of the natural world, a constant striving to maintain the complex interconnections upon which culture, daily comforts, and sometimes even survival depended. Monumental ruins speak to both aspects of this perpetual struggle: On the one hand they are preeminent symbols of human achievement, masterpieces of technological skill and the control of vast manpower and resources; on the other hand, they are vivid reminders of the

"I love above all the sight of vegetation resting upon old ruins; this embrace of nature, coming swiftly to bury the work of man the moment his hand is no longer there to defend it, fills me with deep and ample joy."

—GUSTAVE FLAUBERT, FRENCH NOVELIST, NINETEENTH CENTURY

The Sphinx as it appeared to Napoleon and his men on their ill-fated expedition to Egypt in 1798.
(Reprinted with permission from Monuments of Egypt, *copyright ©1987, Princeton Architectural Press, New York.)*

inevitable triumph of time over the works of man, of the irresistible decay that gnaws away at all things great and small.

This perennial tension that ruins embody, the tension between transience and persistence, order and disorder, has long captivated us. Up through the early Middle Ages, the fallen wreckage of the Colossus of Rhodes, an enormous bronze statue from the third century B.C. that was comparable in size to the Statue of Liberty, was a major attraction for tourists, who marveled at the great cavities that gaped in its broken limbs. One of Ramesses's own sons, Prince Khaemwaset I, was a well-known archaeologist of sorts; he studied ancient texts, revived the memory of past pharaohs, and traveled about the Egyptian countryside placing enormous inscriptions—giant outdoor museum labels—upon the crumbling pyramids and temples that he recognized. In his own way, he was trying to put the past back in order, to hold back the encroaching shadows of ignorance that follow close on the heels of physical decay.

In some cases, monuments have persisted for such a long time that they have outlasted everything that once stood around them, and are now completely bereft of the usual debris that might reveal their purpose to us. The megaliths of Stonehenge—which "carry us back beyond all historical recall into the obscurity of an unknown period," in the words of the English painter John Constable—have over the centuries inspired all sorts of theories as to their origins. At various times Stonehenge was thought to have been the grave of King Arthur's legendary father, a coronation hall of the Vikings, or a temple built by the Druids. None of these theories are true; but with so little left for archaeologists to puzzle over, we can still lament of Stonehenge—as did the sixteenth-century historian and antiquarian William Camden—that "the authors of so notable a monument are buried in oblivion."

> "We shape our buildings;
> thereafter they shape us."
>
> —WINSTON CHURCHILL,
> 1960

The megaliths of Stonehenge.
(Credit: Barry Brukoff)

The enigmatic statues of Easter Island.
(Reprinted with permission from
Hans Helfritz's Die Osterinsel,
Fretz & Wasmuth Verlag, Zurich.)

Stonehenge's megaliths, which were shaped, transported, and raised at a time in Britain when there were no metal tools and no horses, weigh as much as forty tons. Like the gaunt monolithic statues of Easter Island, which so perplexed Captain Cook and other European visitors in the eighteenth century and continue to fire the imagination today, stonework on such an immense scale heightens the impression a monument makes on us when it falls into ruin. "[They] seemed to be triumphing over us," wrote Thor Heyerdahl of the Easter Island statues, "and asking: 'Guess how this engineering work was done! Guess how we moved these gigantic figures down the steep walls of the volcano and carried them over the hills to any place on the island we liked!'"

Such impressions are a vital element of the meaning of these monuments, which were consciously designed to inspire awe and wonder in order to impress rival powers or subject peoples, or simply for posterity. Their builders often succeeded in realizing this goal in ways that they never could have imagined. In 1798 Napoleon and his army, traveling up the Nile to Thebes in riverboats, encountered the sprawling ruins of the Egyptian temples at Karnak. The French archaeologist Dominique Denon wrote that as the boats came within sight of the temples the whole French army suddenly burst into applause, and "stood in amazement [clapping] their hands with delight, as if the end and object of their glorious toils, and the complete conquest of Egypt, were accomplished by taking possession of the splendid remains of this ancient metropolis." The temples at Karnak, a vast field of walls, obelisks, colossi, and sphinx-lined processional avenues, were indeed impressive, composing one of the largest places of worship in the ancient world. Yet there were still monuments that were said to have surpassed them.

The Wonders of the Ancient World

In the Greek-speaking world a few centuries before the birth of Christ there came to be known a group of monuments that were particularly awe-inspiring, whether because of their artistry, the engineering skill evident in their construction, or their sheer scale. These were the Seven Wonders of the Ancient World. Although several writers drew up lists of the Wonders, the list that eventually became set during the Renaissance included the following:

- **The Great Pyramid of Khufu at Gîza** (c. 2551–2470 B.C.), one of humankind's greatest architectural achievements and the tallest building in the world for more than four thousand years.
- **The Hanging Gardens** (c. 810–560 B.C.), a series of extensive and ornate landscaped terraces in northern Iraq.
- **The Statue of Zeus at Olympia** (c. 430 B.C.), a 40-foot-tall gold and ivory statue that was the most celebrated artistic work on mainland Greece.
- **The Temple of Artemis at Ephesus** (c. fourth century B.C.), a Greek temple famous for its imposing size and magnificent sculpture.
- **The Mausoleum at Halicarnassus** (c. 352 B.C.), the 140-foot-high monumental tomb of the Anatolian king Mausolus.
- **The Colossus of Helios at Rhodes** (c. 290 B.C.), a huge bronze statue built on the island of Rhodes to commemorate a military victory.
- **The Pharos of Alexandria** (c. 280 B.C.), the largest and most famous lighthouse of the ancient world, built for a Greek king ruling Egypt.

The idea of creating a list of architectural wonders arose following Alexander the Great's conquest of much of the known world in the fourth century B.C., which gave Greek travelers access to the older civilizations of the Egyptians, Persians, and Babylonians. The Greeks did not initially conceive of these monuments as "Wonders" (Greek *thaumata*) but rather as "sights" or "things to be seen" (*theamata*); in essence, they were the dramatic monuments that filled the travel guidebooks of the ancient world. Since Greek writers had compiled the original lists, many were Greek monuments. Subsequent writers drew up their own lists, replacing the Pharos, for instance, with the Walls of Babylon. Ancient authors report

"I reflected with a mingling of excitement, pleasure and apprehensiveness that I was in one of the most extraordinary locations on the earth, amid places that partake of the fabulous, the very names of which, recited since childhood, have assumed gigantic and almost magical significance."

—Michel-Ange Lancret's impressions at the ruins of Philae in Egypt, 1798

6

The Pyramids at Gîza, the only surviving Wonder of the Ancient World.
(Credit: Robertson and Beato, 1857. Reprinted from D'Alain D'Hooghe's Les Trois Grandes Egyptiennes, Les Pyramids de Gizeh, Marval Publishers, France.)

that these walls were about 40 miles long and 82 feet in height, and that a four-horse chariot could be reversed on the roadway that ran atop them. The Roman poet Martial added the Colosseum to the list, and the Christian bishop Gregory of Tours added Solomon's Temple in Jerusalem. Of course, all of these writers could list only the things they had heard of or seen. Had they walked for a thousand miles beneath the ramparts of the earliest Great Wall of China and still not come close to its end, their lists might have been different.

It is a sad truth that all but one of the Wonders of the Ancient World, the most celebrated architectural achievements of antiquity, have been overcome by time, nature, and the hand of man. An earthquake toppled the Colossus only 65 years after its construction, and it lay in ruins for nearly a thousand years until its remains were scrapped and carried off on the backs of 900 camels to be melted down. Christian Crusaders plundered the ruins of the Mausoleum at Halicarnassus in the sixteenth century and built a fort out of its remains, and only a few scattered stones are left from the Temple of Artemis, said to have been the most elegant of the Wonders. The fate of the celebrated statue of Zeus at Olympia, which presided over the early Olympic games, is unknown, and debate still continues over the site of the Hanging Gardens. Only the ruined pyramids, whose unshakable bulk would seem to preclude annihilation, have survived. Although medieval Muslims stripped them of their outer casings of smooth white limestone to build bridges and houses in Cairo, the pyramids still stand relatively intact, impressive memorials to the might of the Old Kingdom pharaohs. Yet even their survival was not always certain; the nineteenth-century tyrant Mohammed Ali, who obliterated many of Egypt's greatest temples for their stone in order to build factories and modernize his country, once made similar plans to tear down the Great Pyramid—and probably would have done so, had it been economical.

That the pyramids at Gîza are the only extant Wonder of the Ancient World might give us pause. Can we be certain that there was never a monument that surpassed them?

"Antiquities are some remnants of history that have casually escaped the shipwreck of time."

—FRANCIS BACON,
ENGLISH STATESMAN
AND PHILOSOPHER,
SEVENTEENTH CENTURY

Intriguingly, in the historical literature there are in fact scattered references to a lost Egyptian monument that was more impressive than the pyramids. Said to have been one of the most notable monuments the Egyptians ever erected, it now lies buried in oblivion. It was the Cult Complex and Mortuary Temple of Pharaoh Amenemhet III—otherwise known as the Egyptian Labyrinth.

The Marvel that Surpassed the Pyramids

"I visited this building, and found it to surpass description; for if all the walls and other great works of the Greeks could be put together in one, they would not equal, either for labor or expense, this Labyrinth. The Pyramids likewise surpass description, and are severally equal to a number of the greatest works of the Greeks, but the Labyrinth surpasses the Pyramids."

—HERODOTUS, FIFTH CENTURY B.C. GREEK HISTORIAN, WRITING ON THE LOST EGYPTIAN LABYRINTH

According to the fifth-century B.C. Greek historian Herodotus, who stated that he himself had seen the building, the Egyptian Labyrinth was a vast structure on the shores of a large lake located seven days' journey up the Nile from the pyramids at Gîza. It contained 3,000 rooms, half above ground and half below ground, divided into twelve great courts. The entire building was roofed with stone and its walls were covered with sculpture, and adjacent to it a 240-foot-high pyramid decorated with colossal figures was connected to the temple by a subterranean passage. Herodotus emphatically presents the building as a marvel or wonder (*thaumata*) that eclipsed the pyramids or any of the achievements of the Greeks.

To the Greeks in the fifth century B.C., the word *labyrinth* probably meant a large, impressive building with many rooms and connecting passageways, a chaotic and confusing place for those trapped within it. Whether such passageways were intentionally designed to lead people astray, or whether they did so simply because of their overwhelming numbers, is not clear. The Greeks may have derived this word from *labrus*, the sacred double-ax symbol found at the Minoan Palace of Knossos on Crete (c. 2000–1400 B.C.). This palace was a vast interconnected complex that some ancient authors claimed was inspired by the Egyptian Labyrinth.

The first-century B.C. Greek geographer Strabo is the only other eyewitness to the Egyptian Labyrinth whose account has survived. Strabo called it "a great palace composed of many palaces" and marveled at the enormity of the stone slabs that made up its roof and walls. He wrote that it had many great courts, each with its own entrance, but that "in front of the entrances are crypts, as it were, which are long and numerous and have winding passages communicating with one another, so that no stranger can find his way either into any court or out of it without a guide." Climbing atop the building, Strabo saw the great "plain of stone" that formed its roof, and gazed out on the pyramid decorated with colossal figures that Herodotus had described four hundred years earlier—the pyramid of Pharaoh Amenemhet III.

The few clues that we have indicate that the Labyrinth originally served many different purposes for the Egyptians. It certainly contained Amenemhet's mortuary temple, the

Labyrinth of the Minoan Palace at Knossos

Thought by ancient authors to have been modeled on the lost Egyptian Labyrinth
Crete, 2000 to 1400 B.C.

AMAZEING ART: *Wonders of the Ancient World,* by Chris Berg · HarperCollins*Publishers*

An inlaid bronze bust of Amenemhet III, the pharaoh whose imposing mortuary temple became known as the Egyptian Labyrinth.

(Credit: AKG/Collection of George Ortiz)

place on earth where Egyptians could make daily offerings to his spirit, thereby guaranteeing his prosperity in the afterlife. To ensure that this occurred, Amenemhet provided the temple with a staff of priests and endowed them with land, so that they and their descendants could continue to serve him for all eternity. The Labyrinth also functioned as a cult center and meeting place for the rulers of the *nomes*, or Egyptian political divisions, and it may have served as a palace and administrative center too.

Herodotus relates that the lower levels of the Egyptian Labyrinth, which he was not allowed to visit and could speak of only from hearsay, contained the "sepulchers of the kings who built the Labyrinth, and those of the sacred crocodiles." This is quite a plausible story, for the Egyptians are known to have buried sacred bulls in winding underground passages beneath other temples. Also, the inhabitants of the surrounding territories worshipped the crocodile god, Sobek; in the nearby city of Crocodilopolis priests even kept an enormous tame crocodile in whom Sobek was believed to be incarnate. This beast was hounded by its attendants, who, according to Strabo, ran around the shores of the small lake it lived in trying to feed it "a kind of cookie and some roasted meat."

The upper levels of the Egyptian Labyrinth were already more than 1,300 years old at the time of Herodotus's visit, and were likely in a state of partial disrepair. It was probably a vast, sprawling collection of interconnected buildings, shrines, passageways, and courtyards, some decaying, some still maintained. Here is the historian's own description of the interior: "The upper chambers I saw with my own eyes, and found them to excel all other human productions; for the passages through the houses, and the varied windings of the paths across the courts excited in me infinite admiration as I passed from the courts into chambers, and from the chambers into colonnades, and from the colonnades into fresh houses, and again from these into courts unseen before."

Although neither Herodotus nor Strabo knew it, the winding passages that so impressed them were not the only labyrinth nearby. The most fantastic labyrinth of all was hidden from them, buried deep within a building that neither of these Greek visitors would ever have been allowed to enter. This labyrinth protected the mummy of Pharaoh Amenemhet III from tomb robbers, and it was located inside his pyramid.

Like all the pharaohs, Amenemhet believed that his burial chamber had to contain valuable objects if he was to be comfortable in the afterlife. But he had learned his lesson from the fates of earlier pharaohs, who had attempted to safeguard their burial chambers mainly by plugging interior passages with massive granite blocks. Tomb robbers had simply tunneled through the softer limestone surrounding these blocks, so pharaohs in Amenemhet's time turned to a new strategy—they sculpted the interiors of their pyramids into fantastic life-size labyrinths hewn from stone, complete with secret sliding doors, false passageways, and hidden chambers.

Amenemhet's pyramid, which was only slightly smaller than Herodotus said it was, contained one of the most challenging of all such labyrinths. You entered it from a descending stairway hidden on its south side, which led to a small chamber. This apparently led nowhere; the hidden exit was in the roof of the chamber, which concealed a sliding stone trapdoor. This led to an upper chamber that opened into a wide passageway completely filled in by massive stone blocks. One thief had laboriously carved through these blocks, only to discover he had been tricked—the passageway was a dead end. The correct path was a corridor closed only by a wooden door, which opened into a dead-end passage; to get out of this passage you had to find a hidden sliding stone. The sliding stone opened into a bare room; from here a secret trapdoor led to a long passageway. This passageway was filled in with massive stone blocks at its far end, which suggested it might lead somewhere important; even better, two open burial shafts gaped in its floor. One of these shafts was completely filled in by stone slabs, apparently concealing the burial chamber itself, while the other shaft was empty. The correct route, however, was actually a secret door concealed back in the middle of the long passageway. Those who managed to get through all this were greeted with a burial chamber hollowed out of a single huge piece of stone and capped by a 45-ton granite slab.

Somehow, tomb robbers managed to penetrate all of these defenses. After plundering the burial chamber of its valuables, in understandable revenge they set fire to Amenemhet's embalmed body, totally obliterating his spirit in the afterlife. Amenemhet, however, fared no

"May the face of the king be opened so that he may see the Lord of the Horizon when he crosses the sky. May he cause the king to shine like a god, lord of eternity, indestructible."

—INSCRIPTION ON AMENEMHET III'S PYRAMIDION, NINETEENTH CENTURY B.C.

worse than any other pharaoh; tomb robbers got them all, and no mummy of any pharaoh has ever been found in any pyramid.

Amenemhet's pyramid still stands, considerably worse for wear, but time has not spared the Egyptian Labyrinth. The temple complex fell into ruin at an unknown date, and in Roman times it became the site of quarrying for its fine stone. This occupied such a number of masons that a small town sprung up on the site. When the British archaeologist Flinders Petrie excavated the site in 1888, he found nothing but a vast field of chipped stone, six feet deep. "All over an immense area of dozens of acres, I found evidence of a grand building," he wrote. "In every pit I dug there was the flat bed for a pavement either of clean flat sand, or usually of rammed stone chips, forming a sort of concrete . . . in all parts a deep mass of chips of the finest limestone lay upon it." Petrie could only guess that this structure once measured an enormous 1,000 by 800 feet, and he summed up his findings quite succinctly: "From such very scanty remains it is hard to settle anything." Not long after Petrie wrote this, much of the field of limestone chips was quarried away and used as bedding under railway lines, and with almost nothing now remaining on the site, archaeologists can no longer confirm Petrie's measurements. Thus we have only the word of three eyewitnesses— Herodotus, Strabo, and Petrie—to attest to the size and magnificence of a monument that once surpassed the pyramids.

THE LABYRINTH PUZZLES

In this book we inspire you with the artistry of over 30 labyrinths depicting the ruins of architectural wonders from the distant past, most of which have fared somewhat better than the Egyptian Labyrinth. The enduring monuments of past civilizations around the world, they range from third-millennium B.C. Sumerian temples in Iraq to seventh-century A.D. Mayan pyramids in the Americas. In the accompanying essays we reveal the broad sweep of history from which these monuments arose, explore some of the methods of their construction, and ponder their eventual fates. Above all, however, we take a look at these monuments as their builders experienced and lived with them.

The puzzles in this book, with their numerous false pathways leading to dead ends, are usually called mazes. The distinction between mazes, which have dead ends, and labyrinths, which do not, is a modern one, and these puzzles have been inspired by the original meaning of the word labyrinth. In the ancient world, the labyrinth often signified an inextricable construction that was chaotic and confusing for those trapped within it, but that revealed its order and artistry to those able to see its pattern from afar. Being lost in a labyrinth like the one pictured on the next page is indeed confusing, but the artistry of its pattern is also apparent: in this case, some ruins in the Roman Forum. The same juxtaposition of order and disorder, of artistry and chaos, that is apparent in such crumbling ruins is also manifest in the labyrinth itself, for labyrinths are a form of planned chaos, and, like ruins, they are inherently ambiguous.

Your goal while navigating the puzzles is to go from the Start symbol (S) to the End symbol (E). Every line in the artwork is part of the labyrinth, and you will have to explore numerous false passages, likely retracing your steps here and there, before you find the golden thread that leads to your goal. Some of the puzzles are easy to solve, most will tax your abilities, and a few are dazzlingly difficult. If you give up you can always look in the back of the book, where the solutions to the labyrinths are presented. In some of the labyrinths you will notice a small man, with one arm raised, pointing to a part of the monument. This is a six-foot-tall man drawn to scale, allowing you to visualize the actual size of these impressive architectural achievements from the ancient world. Finally, if you become captivated by the stories behind these monuments or by the history of the labyrinth, you can consult the bibliography at the end of the book. Here you will find reading material on every subject from Stonehenge to the Roman aqueducts.

A drawing by fifteenth-century Venetian doctor Giovanni Fontana, the earliest known representation of a maze with false passages leading to dead ends. (Reprinted with permission from Hermann Kern's Labyrinthe, *Prestel Verlag, Munich.)*

13

Order, Chaos, and the Artistry of the Labyrinth
Crumbling Ruins in the Roman Forum, 200 B.C.

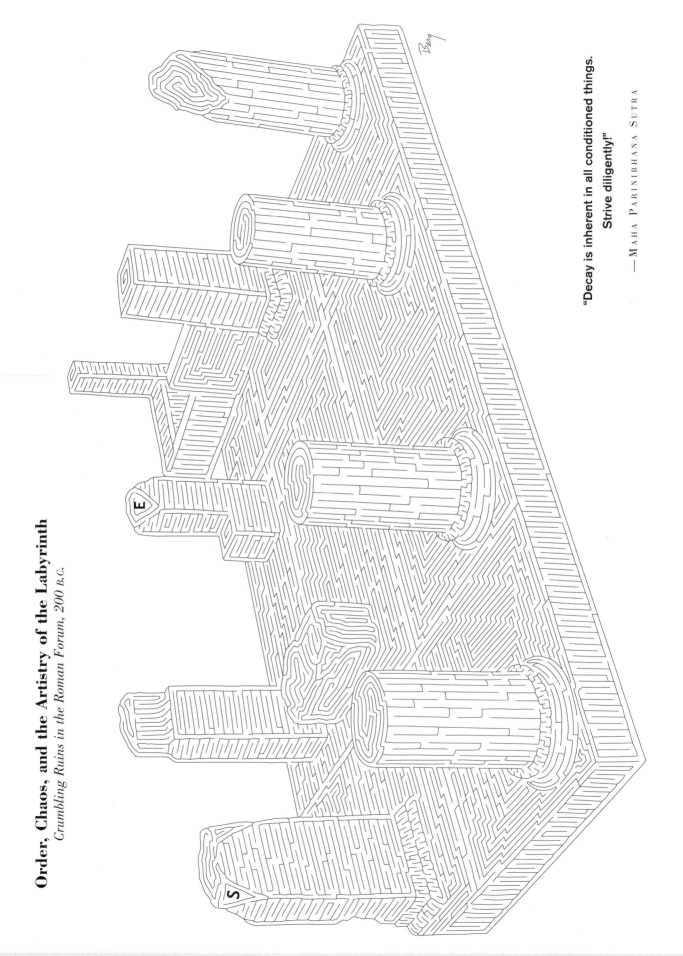

"Decay is inherent in all conditioned things. Strive diligently!"

— MAHA PARINIBHANA SUTRA

AMAZEing ART: Wonders of the Ancient World, by Chris Berg ▪ HarperCollins*Publishers*

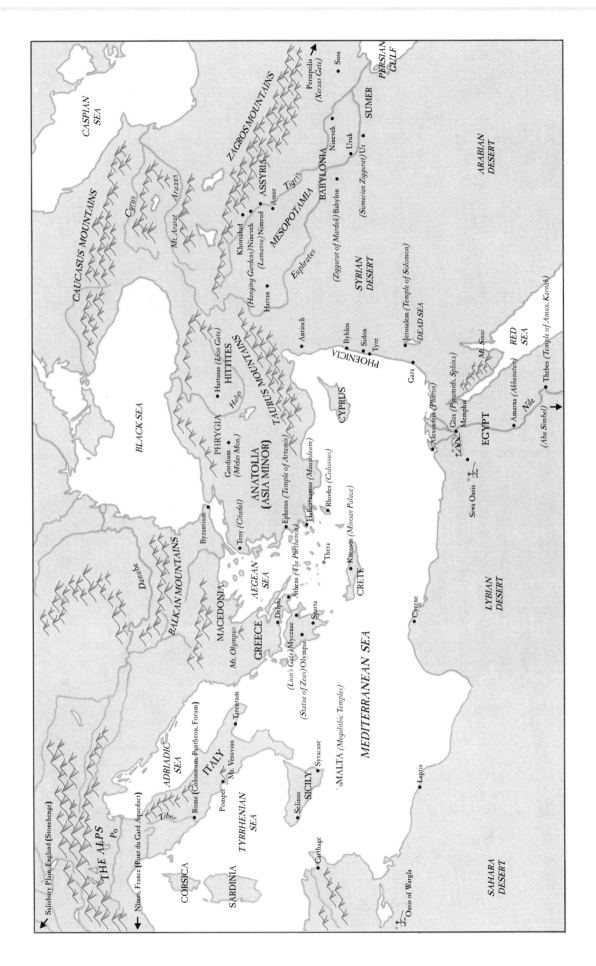

The Wonders of the Ancient World

THE MEGALITH BUILDERS

STONEHENGE AND
THE WONDROUS ENGINES
OF THE WIZARD MERLIN

Stonehenge is one of the oldest and most mysterious archaeological sites in the world. Solitary in the midst of the chalk uplands of southern England, five giant trilithons—two vertical stones with a third lintel laid atop—stand at the focus of a ring of upright stones one hundred feet in diameter. The largest stones weigh over 40 tons, and visitors since Roman times have been baffled by their purpose and the secrets of their construction.

Although Stonehenge is not the only stone circle in Britain, it is one of the most impressive, and through the ages all sorts of theories have purported to explain its origins. In 1136 the medieval English chronicler Geoffrey of Monmouth wrote that its megaliths (from the Greek word for "large stones") had been brought to Ireland by an army of giants from Africa. From there he believed they had been transported to England by the "wondrous engines" of the wizard Merlin. Geoffrey also wrote that the grave of Uther Pendragon, King Arthur's legendary father, lay beneath the stones. In 1650 a leading architect under King James I stated that Stonehenge had actually been a Roman temple. Another authority proclaimed that it had been built by Danish kings when the Vikings overran England in the ninth century A.D., and had been used for coronations. Undoubtedly the most popular theory, however, was first offered by the antiquarian John Aubrey in 1666. He argued that Stonehenge had been built by Celtic priests from Western Europe—the Druids—during Roman times.

Of all these theories, surprisingly it is Geoffrey's tale that contains the most truth. The first structure at Stonehenge was built around 3000 B.C. when ancient Britons, using deer antlers for picks, dug a simple circular ditch and earth bank. They surrounded this with a ring of 56 evenly spaced wooden posts (now called "Aubrey posts") and then erected two parallel entry stones to the northeast. The great circle of megaliths appeared about a thousand years later. Precisely how such enormous stones were dragged overland to Stonehenge from the Marlborough Downs 20 miles away remains unknown, but they were likely erected by being eased into sloping pits and

The Megaliths of Stonehenge
Mysteries of a 5,000-Year-Old Stone Circle
Salisbury Plain, England, Third Millennium B.C.

AMAZEing ART: Wonders of the Ancient World, by Chris Berg ✚ HarperCollinsPublishers

then pulled upright with the aid of ropes. Yet all this occurred long before Danish kings, Romans, or Druids ever appeared in England.

Sometime between 2000 and 1500 B.C., however, a large number of bluestone pillars were erected in two arcs near the center of Stonehenge. The source of these unusual stones remained unknown until 1923, when an English geologist discovered their origin: the Preseli mountains in Wales, over 240 miles away. In the 1920s archaeologists also discovered that the Aubrey post holes contained cremation burials. Amazingly, Geoffrey's fanciful story—of wizards and hidden burials and stones being transported great distances—may thus be a distorted folk memory of the actual building of a part of Stonehenge.

The most controversial aspect of Stonehenge involves its astronomical alignments. It has long been known that a person standing at the center of the stone circle will see the sun rise over the so-called "Heel Stone" on the summer solstice. In the 1960s, however, some eminent astronomers argued that the lunar alignments at Stonehenge proved that it was used to predict eclipses. One astronomer even referred to Stonehenge as a "Neolithic computer." Many others have contested this remarkable conjecture, and believe that Stonehenge was simply a ceremonial center. Some of the lunar alignments involve joining together features from different periods in the monument's history, and statistical analysis has also shown that there may be fewer alignments than could be expected by chance alone.

Cold and silent, the megaliths at Stonehenge leave us few clues to resolve the issue, and we may never know with certainty what secrets lie hidden in their crumbling patterns. But the megalith builders left hundreds of other puzzles scattered across the British Isles and Northern France, such as the stone circles at Callanish and Castlerigg, the rows of menhirs at Carnac, and the Newgrange tomb in Ireland. Perhaps these hold the key that will someday decode Stonehenge.

"The mysterious monument of Stonehenge, standing remote on a bare and boundless heath, as much unconnected with the events of past ages as it is with the uses of the present, carries you back beyond all historical recall into the obscurity of an unknown period."

—JOHN CONSTABLE, ENGLISH PAINTER, 1835

THE ENIGMATIC STONE
TEMPLES OF MALTA

An isolated, wind-swept, and rocky island might appear to be an odd place to find the remains of some of the earliest monuments ever constructed. Yet the small island of Malta, rising like a great plateau from the glistening Mediterranean, was once home to a complex Stone Age civilization that erected enormous multilobed temples and carved vast labyrinthine burial complexes out of the solid rock. From their origins in the fifth millennium B.C. its people flourished for over two thousand years, only to suddenly disappear—almost without a trace—around the time that the Egyptians began building the pyramids at Gîza.

Each of the Maltese temples, which are older than Stonehenge, consists of a series of rounded rooms that are centrally linked in a trefoil plan, much like a clover plant. Often dramatically sited on bluffs overlooking valleys or the sea, they are surrounded by massive cyclopean enclosure walls so huge that local villagers long considered them the work of antediluvian giants. The largest of the temples is Ggantija ("Tower of the Giants"), which dates from about 3600 B.C. Its massive 40-ton limestone blocks dominate the landscape, and were transported to the site on heavy stone ball bearings that can still be found discarded nearby. The temple's builders did not possess metal of any kind, so the huge blocks were cut and dressed with antler picks and heavy stone mallets—an undertaking that must have required decades to complete. Ggantija's inner rooms were covered in lime plaster and painted a deep red, and the temple was likely topped with a timber roof. Despite its monumentality the overall impression is one of comfortable solidity, for straight lines were rarely used in its construction.

The Maltese temples are the earliest known megalithic buildings discovered by archaeologists, and they are full of enigmas. The meaning of the numerous spiral designs, often carved in pairs near the entrances to temple chambers, eludes us. Also unknown is the function of the small rooms found between inner and outer temple walls, with tiny holes linking them to the massive interior chambers. Were these used to accept donations, dispense temple products, or perhaps pronounce oracles? And what was the function of the secret stairway hidden within the wall of one of the struc-

"The inhabitants commonly call them towers (*torri*). They are said to have been piled up by Giants; that is practically all that tradition has to say on the subject."

—ALBERT MAYR, HISTORIAN AND ARCHAEOLOGIST, 1908

Ggantija and the Megalithic Temples on Malta
Ruins of a Lost Stone Age Civilization
Malta, 3600 to 2500 B.C.

tures? The temples themselves seem to have been modeled after burial caves carved by the island's earliest inhabitants, which suggests links to a cult of the dead. Yet figurines from some temples apparently show people suffering from various ailments, implying a healing cult of some kind. To further complicate matters, a row of what appear to be primitive stone-grinding mills found at Ggantija indicates that this site, at least, might have been used to process and store grain. And one of the temples, Mnajdra, appears to have been precisely aligned with the heavens, and has been called "the world's oldest calendar." Theories abound, and until we learn more from further excavations, the enigmas will likely remain. Whatever purpose these temples served, altars found in many of them—along with the burnt bones of sheep, goats, and pigs—show that animal sacrifices definitely took place.

Nor are the temples the only puzzles on the island. Among Malta's most intriguing finds are the island's many rotund figurines, which have been interpreted by many as images of the "Great Goddess," an ancient mother deity who was believed to be an eternally fruitful source of everything. Some believe this Goddess to be the forerunner of the many female deities of Egypt, Mesopotamia, Greece, and Rome, and that the Stone Age civilization of Malta was a matrilineal society. They view the bulging Maltese temples as being modeled after the Great Goddess herself, perhaps representing the "cosmic womb" or the continuous state of pregnancy and fertility of the Goddess. Critics of this theory point out that the figurines from Malta are actually no more female than male—they are simply rotund—and may thus symbolize power, wealth, or status rather than fertility and femininity. Stone Age Goddess figurines from other parts of Europe are also often found in problematic contexts, which include rubbish heaps next to primitive houses. Did such figurines represent a universal mother goddess, or were they simply children's toys, the "Barbie dolls" of the ancient world? It is a tantalizing mystery.

Whatever goddess or god the inhabitants of Malta worshipped, it did not save them from catastrophe, for around 2500 B.C. the island's enormous temples appear to have been burned to the ground. Over the centuries they were gradually covered over by the earth and their builders were forgotten. By Roman times, Malta was known chiefly for its breed of small dogs, the Maltese.

"Off Pachynus lies Malta, whence come the little dogs called Maltese ... eighty-eight miles distant from the Cape."

—Strabo, Greek geographer, first century B.C.

"There is an island called Malta ... separated from Sicily by a sufficiently wide and perilous navigation, in which there is a town of the same name ... that place, to which the fleets of enemies often came, where pirates are accustomed to winter almost every year ... "

—Cicero, Roman statesman and orator, first century B.C.

THE PYRAMIDS:
TOMBS OF THE PHARAOHS

Egyptian civilization has left no greater monuments than its pyramids, the enduring symbols of the age of the pharaohs. There are actually more than eighty pyramids scattered across Egypt, but the three at Gîza are the earliest, the best preserved, and by far the largest. Built over an astonishingly brief 75-year period by the Old Kingdom pharaohs Khufu, Khafre, and Menkaure in the twenty-sixth century B.C., the Gîza pyramids are masterpieces of technical skill and engineering ability. Khufu's Great Pyramid is the largest of the three. More than two million blocks of limestone, each weighing an average of two and a half tons, went into this mighty structure, yet in places its stonework has finer joints than any other building in ancient Egypt. Its four sides average 756 feet in length and differ by only a few inches, and its edges are aligned to true north to within one tenth of one degree. It is one of mankind's greatest architectural achievements, and at 481 feet in height it was the tallest building in the world for more than four thousand years.

The pyramid shape was closely associated with the Egyptian sun god, Re. Inscriptions within the burial chambers of later pyramids (the "Pyramid Texts") state that when the pharaoh died, the sun would strengthen its beams and create a celestial ramp upon which his spirit would ascend to the heavens. The pyramids symbolized these ramps, and Khufu's own name for his pyramid, Akhet-Khufu ("the Horizon of Khufu"), denoted the point at which the reborn pharaoh would rise again each day as the sun. Like all the pyramids, Khufu's tomb was capped by a *pyramidion*, a single triangular block of stone plated with gold or electrum that might have been inscribed with images of Egyptian deities. The light of the rising and setting sun would brilliantly reflect off this capstone, high above the Gîza plateau, when all else was in shadow.

Vast as it is, Khufu's pyramid is only one part of a much larger funerary complex that includes the pyramid itself, smaller satellite pyramids, several boat pits, and an elaborate mortuary temple. Believing that his spirit needed the same food, clothing, and valuables that it had required in this life, Khufu arranged for a permanent staff of priests to make daily offerings at his temple—for all eternity—to promote his

"On the pyramid it is declared in Egyptian writing how much was spent on radishes and onions and leeks for the workmen, and if I rightly remember that which the interpreter said in reading to me this inscription, a sum of one thousand six hundred talents of silver was spent."

—THE GREEK HISTORIAN HERODOTUS, BEING DUPED BY A TOUR GUIDE, FIFTH CENTURY B.C.

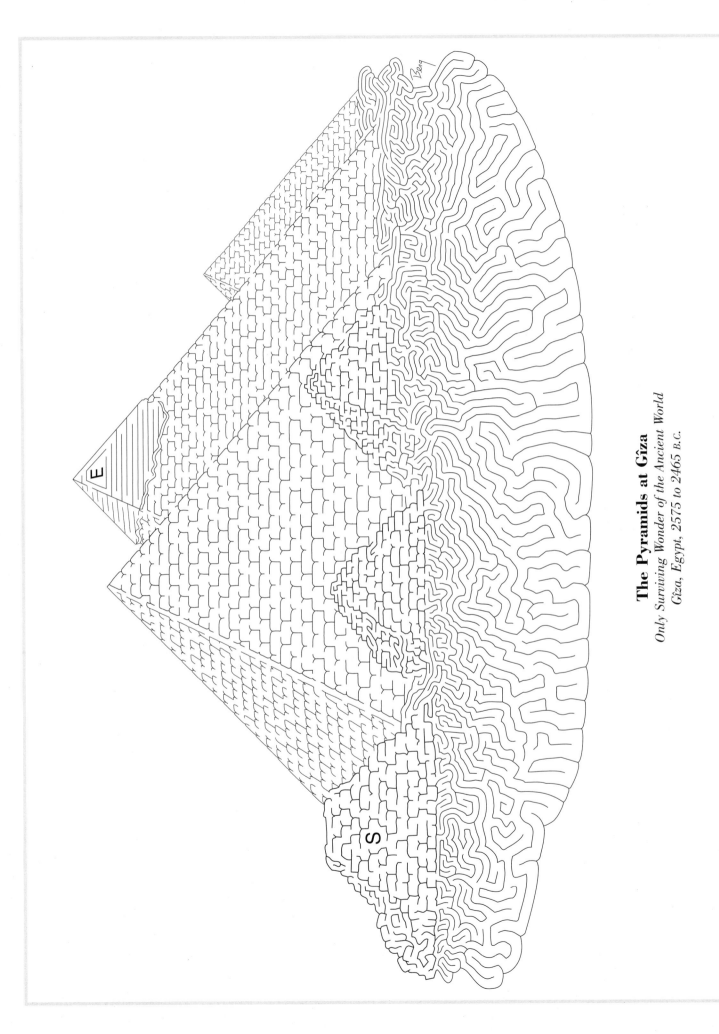

The Pyramids at Gîza

Only Surviving Wonder of the Ancient World

Gîza, Egypt, 2575 to 2465 B.C.

AMAZEing ART: Wonders of the Ancient World, by Chris Berg   HarperCollinsPublishers

welfare in the afterlife. To guarantee the sanctity of his remains and thus ensure his immortality, Khufu also contrived to hide his mummified body in a secret burial chamber deep within his pyramid, guarded from tomb robbers by massive stone barriers.

The question of how the pyramids were built has not been completely resolved. The consensus is that it was done by some sort of ramp system upon which the heavy limestone blocks were hauled on sledges and rollers. Remains of such ramps have been found. Yet Herodotus, who visited the pyramids in the fifth century B.C.—two thousand years after they were built—was told that the ancient engineers "raised the stones with machines." There is some evidence to support this: Many mysterious rounded and grooved stones, commonly found near the pyramids, look very much like simple pulleys. Whatever their methods, it took at least twenty-five thousand men more than twenty years to construct Khufu's Great Pyramid. Contrary to popular belief, the Egyptian rulers did not use slave labor; much of the work was probably done by conscripted farm workers, organized into groups with such inspiring names as "Vigorous Gang" and "Enduring Gang," during the annual flood of the Nile.

Throughout history many fantastic tales have been told about the pyramids. Some Romans considered them superfluous and foolish displays, designed to exhaust the pharaoh's treasuries and deprive their successors of wealth. In the Middle Ages they were thought to be the biblical Granaries of Joseph, built to aid him during the seven lean years. For a long time Arabs considered them libraries containing the wisdom of a long-departed civilization; this belief, however, did not stop medieval Muslim rulers from stripping the monuments of what remained of their outer casings of smooth white limestone, using it to build houses and bridges in Cairo. Nor did it prevent the nineteenth-century tyrant Mohammed Ali from making plans to completely tear down the Great Pyramid for its stone; he was dissuaded only when he discovered that a quarry closer to Cairo would be more efficient.

"Man fears time, yet time fears the pyramids."

—Arab Proverb

"The appearance of these ancient monuments that have survived the destruction of nations, the fall of empires, the ravages of time, inspires a kind of reverence. The soul glances over the centuries that have flowed past their unshakable bulk and experiences an involuntary shudder of awe."

—Claude Etienne Savary, French General and Administrator, *Letters on Egypt*, 1786

THE GLIMMERING LIGHT
OF HISTORY

In the shadow of the Pyramids, on the edge of the Gîza plateau, sits one of Egypt's most extraordinary monuments—the Great Sphinx. Carved out of the natural bedrock and enlarged with blocks of limestone, this enormous statue of a recumbent lion with a human head is the largest surviving sculpture from the ancient world. It is also the earliest colossal sculpture the Egyptians erected, so old that for much of history the Egyptian pharaohs themselves worshipped it as a god.

It is generally accepted that the Great Sphinx was built by Pharaoh Khafre (c. 2575–2465 B.C.) during the Old Kingdom, the age of the great pyramid-builders. A fragmentary inscription on a nearby stele seems to include the pharaoh's name, and the Sphinx is seamlessly integrated into the surrounding temple complex built by Khafre. There is speculation that the monument may be older than this, however, for an inscription within the Great Pyramid, dating from 600 B.C., records that Pharaoh Khufu—Khafre's father—carried out repairs on the Sphinx's tail and headdress. Some believe that the Sphinx may have been built by Khufu; others date it as far back as 3100 B.C., before the unification of Upper and Lower Egypt, and think that the Old Kingdom temples were simply built around it. If so, the Sphinx would predate the earliest phase of Stonehenge, and be among the most ancient monuments from antiquity that have survived intact into modern times.

The original purpose of the Sphinx is unknown. It may have been built to symbolically guard over the Gîza plateau, and it may have been a portrait of Pharaoh Khafre. Its face seems to bear a resemblance to Khafre's, and the royal headdress that it wears is particular to pharaohs. Facing east, the Sphinx is aligned with the rising sun each morning, and later Egyptian rulers worshipped it as an aspect of the sun god, calling it Hor-Em-Akhet (meaning "Horus of the Horizon"). A small chapel between its outstretched paws contained dozens of inscribed stelae placed by the pharaohs to honor the god. One of these recounts a dream that Thutmose IV had while taking a nap in the shade of the monument, in which the Sphinx came to him and promised him the crown of Egypt if he would only dig it out of the sand that was engulfing it.

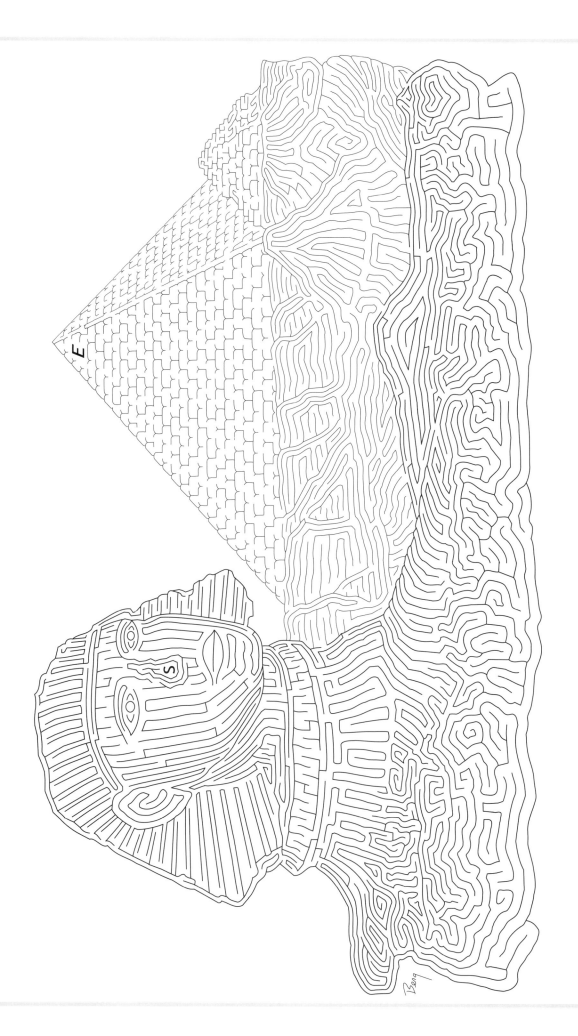

The Riddle of the Sphinx

Earliest Colossal Statue in Egypt
Giza, Egypt, 3100 to 2500 B.C.

(BASED ON AN IMAGE OF THE SPHINX DRAWN BY NAPOLEON'S ARTISTS IN 1798.)

AMAZEing ART: Wonders of the Ancient World, by Chris Berg. ▦ HarperCollinsPublishers

The Sphinx was carved out of the bedrock with stone hammers and copper chisels, and as it was being sculpted, a large defect was found in the rock near its hindquarters. Its builders extended the body with large blocks of high-quality Tura limestone—the same stone that encases the pyramids—to cover up the fault; as a result, the Sphinx's head is far too small for its 236-foot-long body. Legend recorded that there were secret passages under this elongated body, and archaeologists have in fact found three tunnels beneath it. They seem to date from pharaonic times, but their purpose remains a mystery.

There are several stories explaining the Sphinx's famous missing nose: One is that it fell off when Napoleon's archaeologists were investigating the statue; another is that the Mameluke army used the Sphinx for target practice, and a lucky artillery shot blew it off. Neither of these tales is true. The nose was probably removed in the eighth century A.D. by a Sufi who considered the Sphinx a blasphemous idol, but all that can be said for certain, based on the tool marks that remain, is that it was deliberately pried off with chisels. The Sphinx's face, which in ancient times was painted dark red, was also decorated with a stone beard and displayed a sculpted cobra on its forehead, both of which have fallen off. This may explain why, for much of the Sphinx's later history, its face was interpreted as a woman's.

Even without its nose the Sphinx's battered visage, jutting out of the shifting sands and weathered rock, beckons to us with its enigmatic smile and watchful eyes. Over the last five millennia the Sphinx has gazed out upon the builders of the pyramids and the armies of Ramesses II, Greek soldiers under Alexander, and Romans under Caesar. It has watched Napoleon and his men as they passed by on their ill-fated expedition in the land of the pharaohs, and seen British armies marching off to fight Rommel in World War II. Visitors from Herodotus to Mark Twain have gazed upon its face in the setting sun, pondering the glimmering light of history that, slowly receding into the distance, fades into the unknowable past.

"In front of the pyramids is the Sphinx, which is perhaps even more to be admired than they. It impresses one by its stillness and silence, and is the local divinity of the inhabitants of the surrounding district."

—PLINY THE ELDER, ROMAN AUTHOR AND STATESMAN, FIRST CENTURY A.D.

THEBES,
"THE MOST ESTEEMED
OF PLACES"

The largest of all Egyptian temples, and one of the largest places of worship in the ancient world, was the Temple of Amun at Karnak, the northern half of the ancient city of Thebes on the Nile. The Egyptians called this place Ipet-Esut, which meant "the Most Esteemed of Places," and it was actually not one temple but a great complex of temples, added to and altered over a 2000-year period. Few ruins in all of Egypt make a more overwhelming impression than this vast field of walls, obelisks, columns, colossi, gateways, and sphinx-lined processional avenues.

Amun was a local deity who grew to become the principal national god of Egypt after Theban kings, expelling foreign rulers known as the Hyksos, reunited the country in the sixteenth century B.C. His name meant "the Hidden One," and other Egyptian gods were seen as manifestations of his power. On reliefs and paintings he was painted blue to denote invisibility, for his true appearance was thought to be unknowable. As his cult grew in importance over the centuries, succeeding pharaohs vied to outdo each other's building projects at Karnak, and erected ever grander monuments dedicated to the god.

The most impressive part of the Temple of Amun, and one of the greatest architectural wonders of antiquity, is the famous Hypostyle Hall. This enclosed hall, begun by Seti I and completed by his son Ramesses II, was larger than a modern-day football field. Its stone roof was supported by a forest of 134 enormous columns, the largest of which are 73 feet tall, over 30 feet in circumference, and topped by 12-foot-wide foliage capitals upon which one hundred men can stand. In ancient times, the only light in the hall came from a few small windows high up by the roof, which illuminated the column's smooth white surfaces and colorful reliefs with the same distant, diffuse glow that fills modern cathedrals.

The Hypostyle Hall led to the innermost shrine of the temple—an area where no commoners were allowed—that housed a solid-gold statue of Amun. The temple priests believed that if they took proper care of Amun, he in turn would look

"It is difficult to describe the noble and stupendous ruins of Thebes. Beyond all others they give you the idea of a ruined, yet imperishable city; so vast is their extent, that you wander a long time confused and perplexed, and discover at every step some new objects of interest."

—JOHN CARNE,
ENGLISH TRAVELER
AND WRITER, 1826

The Temple of Amun at Karnak
*One of the Largest Temple Complexes in the World
Thebes, Egypt, 2100 to 300 B.C.*

aMAZEing ART: Wonders of the Ancient World, by Chris Berg ⊞ HarperCollinsPublishers

after Egypt, so the statue was clothed and fed, washed, and anointed with oils every day. Once a year a great month-long festival, known as the Festival of Opet, was thrown in the god's honor. An extraordinary series of reliefs at Karnak depicts white-robed priests, surrounded by crowds of worshippers, carrying the statue in a golden bark through the streets of Thebes, thence onto a barge for the journey upriver to Luxor where the feast was held. Women are shown shaking musical rattles, men beating together ivory wands, trumpeters playing fanfares, and others prostrating themselves before the god. Ironically, this statue of Amun the Unknowable, Ruler of Thebes, King of the Gods, was one quarter the size of an adult man—it was a midget. This may have been because a full-size gold statue would have weighed nearly 3,000 pounds, and thus been very difficult to move about.

In addition to keeping tame crocodiles and decorating them with gold jewelry, the priests who looked after Amun had strict rules of ritual purity, which included shaving their entire bodies once every day. When they died, they had lifelike statues of themselves—which embodied their spirits—erected in the temple so that they could continue to be blessed by Amun's presence in the afterlife. Over the centuries these statues grew in number until thousands of them crowded the dark hallways, silent reminders of the immensity of history that had gone before. According to a tale told by Herodotus, a Greek visitor once boasted to the priests that he could trace his own descent through 16 generations; the priests replied by using these statues to trace the descent of their officials through an unbelievable 345 generations.

The great Temple of Amun flourished for nearly two millennia, until in 663 B.C., during a war begun by inexperienced Nubian pharaohs, it was sacked by the Assyrians under King Ashurbanipal. Although it was rebuilt, the temple never fully recovered. By Roman times, Thebes seems to have dwindled to a small village visited by tourists, who came to see the ruins of the ancient temples at this most esteemed of places.

"Those who dwell about Thebes hold [crocodiles] to be most sacred, and these people keep one crocodile selected from the whole number, which has been trained to tameness, and they put hanging ornaments of molten stone and of gold into their ears and anklets round their front feet, and treat them as well as possible while they live, and after they are dead they bury them in sacred tombs, embalming them."

—HERODOTUS, GREEK HISTORIAN, FIFTH CENTURY B.C.

RAMESSES THE GREAT,
BORN OF RE,
BELOVED OF AMUN

"King of Kings am I, [Ramesses]. If anyone would know how great I am . . . let him surpass *one* of my works."

—INSCRIPTION ON THE BASE OF RAMESSES 900-TON COLOSSUS AT THE RAMESSEUM, AS RECORDED BY DIODORUS SICULUS, FIRST CENTURY B.C.

The fame of Ramesses II, one of Egypt's most powerful and capable rulers, was unsurpassed in his own age. Monuments to his glory are scattered all across the land of the pharaohs, from Nubia in the south to Palestine in the north. He reigned for over 65 years and lived to be over ninety years old, fathering more than 100 children, many of whom he outlived. He was an adept administrator, a capable general, and a skilled diplomat. To his subjects he was Usermare Ramesses, protector of Egypt, conqueror of foreign lands, great in victories, born of Re, beloved of Amun; to us, he is Ramesses the Great.

Ramesses assumed the throne in the late thirteenth century B.C., at a time when Egypt was near the height of its power. From the start he was intent on outdoing the reputation of his father, Seti I. A skilled propagandist, he well understood the value of monumental displays of royal power, and possessed a mania for erecting colossal temples and statues dedicated to his deified self—the bigger the better. Across the Nile from ancient Thebes he built the Ramesseum, a great political and theological center that was intended to last for "a million years"; one of its enormous fallen colossi would later inspire Shelley's famous poem "Ozymandias." He built an extensive palace-city in the Nile Delta, completed the enormous Hypostyle Hall at the Temple of Amun at Karnak, enlarged temples in Memphis and Heliopolis, and erected colossi of himself all across Egypt. He built more than any other pharaoh and achieved the immortality he sought, for his fame has endured for more than three thousand years.

In the land of Nubia, long coveted by the Egyptians for its rich deposits of gold, Ramesses built one of his most imposing monuments—the great temple at Abu Simbel. Carved over a 20-year period out of a high sandstone bluff overlooking the Nile, its four enormous seated colossi depict Ramesses himself, and are each surrounded by smaller statues of his favorite wives and children. At 72 feet in height they are among the largest colossal human sculptures the Egyptians ever erected, and

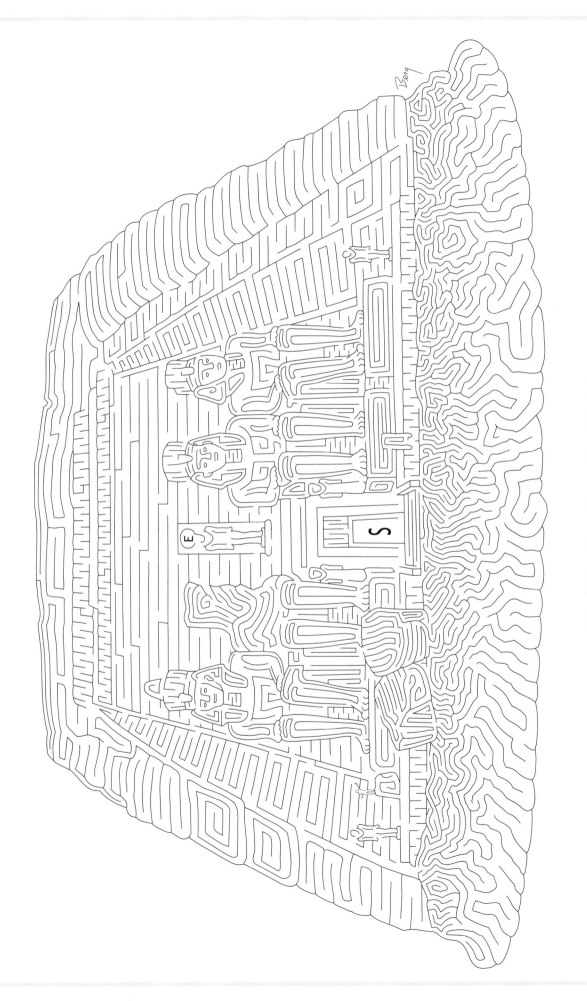

Rock-Cut Temple at Abu Simbel

Imposing Monument of Ramesses II, Greatest of Pharaohs
Upper Nile, Egypt, 1265 B.C.

AMAZEing ART: Wonders of the Ancient World, by Chris Berg ✠ HarperCollins*Publishers*

"O chosen and valiant workers, I know your hand, which carves for me my many monuments. Oh you who cherish working with precious stones of every kind, since you have constructed the monuments, thanks to you I shall be able to adorn all the temples I have erected for the length of their existence . . . I am Ramesses, Beloved of Amun."

—RAMESSES II STELE FROM HELIOPOLIS, THIRTEENTH CENTURY B.C.

clearly exemplify the kind of grandiose architecture Ramesses was fond of. Their carving must have been planned and executed very carefully, for any mistakes in cutting them out of the rock face could not easily have been fixed. One of the colossi was toppled by an earthquake only ten years after the temple was built; its broken pieces were so large, however, that there was little anyone could do to put them back in place, and so they were simply left lying on the ground.

The central doorway of the temple leads to a hallway cut into the mountain, which contains several 30-foot-high ornamented pillars sculpted into the image of Osiris, god of the dead. Twice a year the sun penetrates through this hallway into a chamber deep within the mountain, illuminating a seated statue of Ramesses accompanied by statues of the supreme Egyptian gods Re-Harakhte, Amun-Re, and Ptah— all carved from the solid rock. Nearby walls are decorated with images of Ramesses's military exploits, and like most Egyptian pharaohs, Ramesses always portrayed himself leading his troops to stunning victories. Here in the hallway at Abu Simbel he is shown singlehandedly conquering hordes of Hittite charioteers during the famous battle of Kadesh, which was actually a near-disaster for him that ended, at best, in a draw.

One of the chief wonders of Abu Simbel is its location—the temple was constructed in the middle of nowhere. Unlike the great temples at Thebes, which were the center of a teeming city, or the pyramids at Gîza, which dominated the skyline of Memphis, Abu Simbel was built far up the Nile, deep in the land of Nubia. Its impressive colossi stand alone in the landscape, vast, silent, and brooding. The sudden appearance of the monument to ships sailing down the Nile must have produced astonishment, and caused travelers to wonder: Who would build such a thing, here where there is nothing else? What glories await us, as we journey further into the land of the pharaohs? Today we wonder the same thing, for not all that the Egyptians built has been discovered—by some estimates, we have found only half of their great monuments. The rest lie buried beneath the sands, awaiting discovery.

"The sand from the north side, accumulated by the wind on the rock above the temple, choked the entrance and buried two thirds of it. It was evidently a very large place, but our astonishment increased when we found it to be one of the most magnificent of temples."

—GIOVANNI BELZONI, EXPLORER AND HUNTER OF ANTIQUITIES, 1817

MESOPOTAMIA AND THE ANCIENT NEAR EAST

SUMER,
THE CIVILIZED LAND

Much of Iraq and Syria is a vast flat plain of dried and cracked mud, brown and desolate save for where the Tigris and Euphrates rivers snake through it. A visitor to this country—which the Greeks called "the Land Between the Rivers," or *Mesopotamia*—will search in vain for anything like the monumental wreckage of pharaonic Egypt or the elegant relics of the Greeks. This was the cradle of civilization, where farming and writing first developed, where villages first grew into cities, cities into kingdoms, and kingdoms into empires; yet most of what was built here has long since crumbled into ruin, leaving little but foundations for archaeologists to puzzle over. But there is one notable exception—the Sumerian Ziggurat at Ur.

The Sumerians called themselves Sag-gi-ga, which meant "the Black-headed Ones," and their country Ken-gi-r, "the Civilized Land." By 2000 B.C. Sumerians living in cities such as Ur and Uruk in southern Iraq had developed paved roads, the arch and vault, writing, schools, epic literature, law codes, banking, and even joint-stock corporations. All this occurred two thousand years before Cleopatra or Julius Caesar.

The Ziggurat at Ur, a massive stepped pyramid about 210 by 150 feet in size, is the most well-preserved monument from the remote age of the Sumerians. It consists of a series of successively smaller platforms that once rose to a height of about 64 feet. It was constructed with a solid core of mud-brick covered by a thick skin of burnt-brick to protect it from the elements. Its corners are oriented to the compass points, and—like the Parthenon—its walls slope slightly inward, giving an impression of solidity. The ziggurat was part of a temple complex that served as an administrative center for the city, and it was believed to be the place on earth where the moon god Nanna, the patron deity of Ur, had chosen to dwell. Nanna was depicted as a wise and unfathomable old man with a flowing beard and four horns, and a single small shrine—the bedchamber of the god—was placed upon the ziggurat's summit. This was occupied each night by only one woman, chosen by the

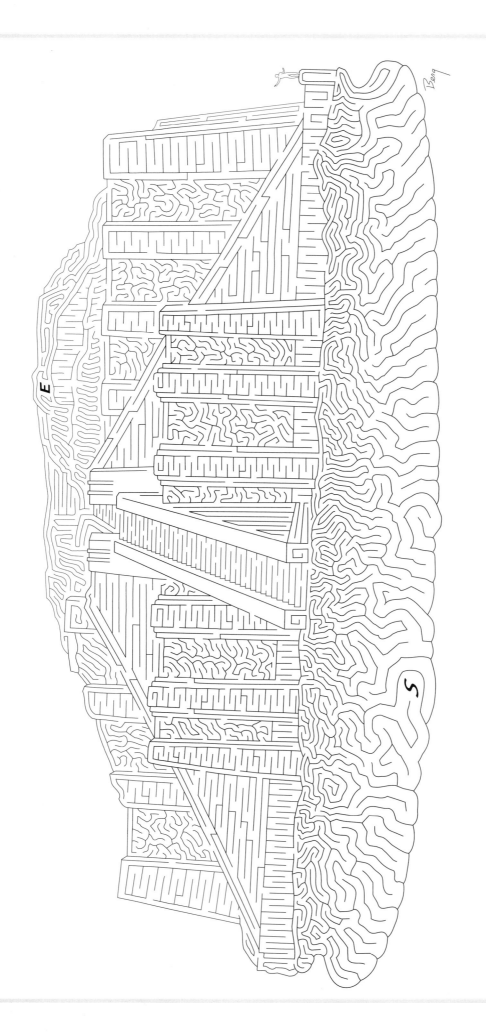

Ruins of the Ziggurat at Ur
Ancient Sumerian Pyramid Temple
Sumer, Iraq, 2200 B.C.

AMAZEING ART: *Wonders of the Ancient World,* by Chris Berg ■ HarperCollins*Publishers*

"On that day, the storm howled, the tempest swirled. Lightning was devoured in heaven alongside the seven winds, and the deafening storm made the earth tremble. The winds on high embraced the waters below, but I, the King, was unafraid, uncowed. Like a lion I was ready to pounce. My heart full of happiness I sped along the course."

—HYMN COMMEMORATING KING SHULGI'S 200-MILE RUN, TWENTY-FIRST CENTURY B.C.

priests from among all the women of the city to be the god's companion. A kitchen, likely used to prepare food for the god, was located at the base of one of the ziggurat's side stairways.

Construction of the ziggurat was completed in the twenty-first century B.C. by King Shulgi, during whose 48-year reign the city of Ur grew to be the capital of an empire controlling much of Mesopotamia. To win the allegiance of the many formerly independent cities he controlled, Shulgi proclaimed himself a god and became a great patron of the arts. He had his poets and scribes publicize all sorts of stories about his prowess: He had complete mastery of every weapon of war, could capture gazelles on the run, slay lions unaided, and play every known musical instrument. The king himself claimed that he once ran 200 miles during a fierce hailstorm—which he may have done.

Shulgi also boasted that he was one of the few kings who had gone to school to become a scribe. The Sumerian method of writing, known as cuneiform, consisted of complex wedge-shaped symbols impressed on clay tablets. At the schools that taught this difficult skill, students also learned how to debate in public and practiced the refined art of insulting opponents before refuting their arguments. "He is spawn of a dog, seed of a wolf, a helpless hyena's whelp, and an addlepated mountain monkey whose reasoning is nonsensical!" begins one such preamble. We can only guess whether Shulgi's fellow students dared ridicule their king—who once wrote of himself, "I am a powerful man who rejoices in his loins!"—in this way.

After Shulgi's time the fortunes of Ur declined. His sons could not hold on to the empire they inherited, and their city was soon sacked by the Elamites. Ur was then ruled by a succession of foreign kings until the fourth century B.C., when the Euphrates river changed its course and the city, lacking irrigation, was abandoned. For the next two thousand years, until nineteenth-century archaeologists discovered its remains, "the Civilized Land" was completely erased from the memory of mankind.

"Behold its outer wall, whose cornice is like copper.

Peer at the inner wall, which none can equal. Seize

upon the threshold, which is ancient, and draw near to

Ianna, the dwelling of Ishtar, which no future king,

no man, can surpass."

—*The Epic of Gilgamesh*, THIRD MILLENNIUM B.C.

THE MYSTERIOUS ORIGINS
OF THE LOST ARK

The Temple of Solomon was built to house the Ark of the Covenant, one of the most sacred objects in all of biblical religion. As is well known, the search for the final resting place of the lost Ark, which disappeared sometime before the sixth century B.C., has captivated mankind for more than two thousand years. The search for its origins, conducted in dusty libraries, is less well known—but far more interesting.

The Ark is typically pictured as a small, gold-lined wooden chest that contained the two stone tablets—brought down by Moses from atop Mount Sinai—on which the ten commandments were engraved. The chest was covered by a thick slab of gold that was adorned with two sculpted kerubs—fierce creatures much like sphinxes—between whose outstretched wings the invisible presence of God was thought to be enthroned. The Ark, which had accompanied the Israelites on their wanderings through the wilderness, was said to generate a powerful divine radiation that destroyed anyone who approached it, and was kept permanently shrouded in darkness within the inaccessible innermost chamber of the Temple of Solomon.

The fascinating idea that the Ark originally contained the ten commandments first surfaced more than six hundred years after the time of Moses, and is almost certainly a legend with little historical basis. The idea was first promoted during the religious reforms of King Josiah in the seventh century B.C., and was used to unify the Israelites around Solomon's Temple. It was a successful story, for no one except the high priest of the Israelites was ever allowed within the innermost chamber of the temple to view the Ark and disprove the story. However, it is only one of three distinct traditions—written down by different authors at different times in history— that are preserved in the Bible concerning the Ark. The most ancient tradition has nothing whatsoever to say about the ten commandments being kept within the Ark; rather, it speaks of the Ark as a divine standard that led the Israelites on their march through the wilderness and in their battles. It was thought to contain the god Yahweh, and, as in later traditions, was considered to be extremely powerful and capable of striking dead anyone who touched it.

"And when they came to the threshing floor of Chidon, Uzzah put out his hand to hold the ark, for the oxen stumbled. And the anger of the Lord was kindled against Uzzah; and he smote him because he put forth his hand to the ark; and he died there before God."

—CHRONICLES 13:9–10

41

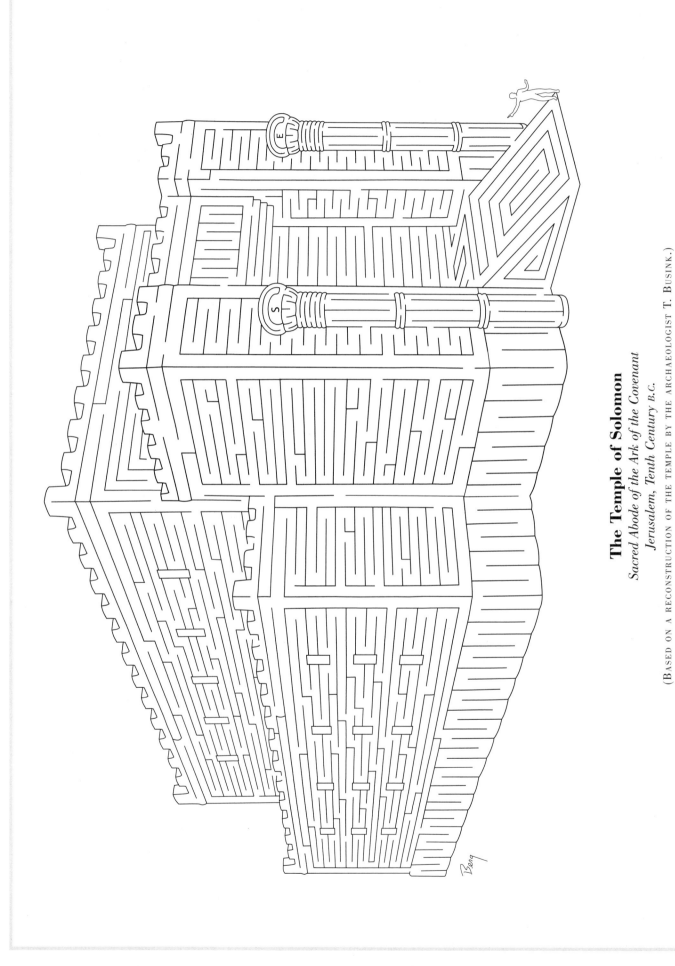

The Temple of Solomon
Sacred Abode of the Ark of the Covenant
Jerusalem, Tenth Century B.C.

(BASED ON A RECONSTRUCTION OF THE TEMPLE BY THE ARCHAEOLOGIST T. BUSINK.)

AMAZEING ART: *Wonders of the Ancient World*, by Chris Berg ▪ HarperCollinsPublishers

The Hebrew word that is sometimes translated as "Ark" actually means "box," and interestingly, this word is used to refer to several other sacred boxes or "Arks" of the tribes of Israel. There are references to a sacred box of great magnificence in the town of Ophrah, at the important Israelite sanctuary of Dan, and at the lesser sanctuary at Nob. These boxes are thought to have been used by priests for divination and to have housed the various tribal gods. The realization that there was more than one box or "Ark" is an ancient heresy, first recognized in the second century A.D. by an unusually perceptive rabbi. Once, each of the twelve tribes of Israel had its own sacred box, and the "Ark of the Covenant" was only one of these: the box belonging to the tribe of Ephraim. Eventually placed in the Temple of Solomon, it was this box that was later purported to contain the two stone tablets of Moses.

Scholars disagree about what was kept within the original Box of Ephraim. Perhaps it housed a primitive image of Yahweh, or two simple stones used for divination, or it might even have been empty. Clearly, however, the box led the Israelites on their earliest tribal migrations and participated in their battles, and a deity was thought to dwell within it. In this respect the box is remarkably similar to the small boxlike tents, carried on the backs of sacred camels, that were used by pre-Canaanite tribes in Syria and Palestine for the same purposes. These small tents, which were said to contain tribal gods, are known to have often housed sacred stones, or betyls.

Betyls were typically worshipped in pairs, and their nature remains obscure. The most persuasive and intriguing theory is that they were fragments of iron meteorites, transported in prehistoric times from the desert. These heavy, silvery-colored stones fell from the heavens causing destruction and creating sulfurous fumes; their fragments, when placed in pairs, appeared to be pushed around by an invisible being—for they were highly magnetic. In the centuries before man discovered iron and its magnetic properties, it would indeed have seemed that these rare magical stones heralded the living presence of a god within the sacred box that housed them. Whether the original Box of Ephraim contained two such stones, transformed in later tradition into Moses's two stone tablets, we will probably never know.

"So they set out from the mount of the Lord three days' journey; and the ark of the covenant of the Lord went before them . . . to seek out a resting place for them. And the cloud of the Lord was over them by day, whenever they set out from the camp. And whenever the ark set out, Moses said, 'Arise, O Lord, and let thy enemies be scattered; and let them that hate thee flee before thee.' "

—NUMBERS 10:33

THE PHOENICIANS,
MASTER SEA TRADERS

Sometime around 1130 B.C. an Egyptian priest named Wen-Amun traveled to the Phoenician city of Byblos to buy cedarwood for a religious festival. The gods were apparently not looking after Wen-Amun, however, for midway through his voyage he was robbed of most of his gold. Worse, when he stepped ashore at Byblos the city's king, Zakar-Baal, refused to barter with him and told him to leave. But Wen-Amun was loath to return to Egypt without completing his mission, so he waited in the harbor at Byblos for his luck to change. For 29 days in a row he endured the same sharply worded message from the king: "Get out [of] my harbor!"

On the thirtieth day, just when Wen-Amun had lost hope and was preparing to return home, the Phoenician king relented and granted him an audience. "I found the king," Wen-Amun writes, "sitting [in] his upper room, with his back turned to a window, so that the waves of the Great Syrian sea broke behind him." Taking out a scroll that recorded past transactions, King Zakar-Baal bluntly pointed out that he had stopped giving tribute to the Egyptians some time ago, and if Wen-Amun wanted timber he had better pay for it. With the king's permission, Wen-Amun was allowed to dispatch a Phoenician messenger to carry word of his situation to his superiors in Egypt and to ask for more funds. In a few months he duly received several jars of gold and silver, twenty sacks of lentils, hundreds of cowhides, ropes, and papyrus rolls, and many other goods. With these items he purchased his cedarwood and then made preparations to return home.

Wen-Amun's adventures, described in an Egyptian papyrus dating from about 1100 B.C., provide us with a rare glimpse of the Phoenicians, the master sea traders of the ancient Mediterranean. A Semitic people related to the Hebrews, the Phoenicians were confined by more powerful neighbors to a narrow strip of land on the coast of Lebanon. Their homeland possessed few natural resources, but these the skilled Phoenician merchants and craftsmen turned to extraordinary effect. Out of the sand on their beaches the Phoenicians created superb glasswork, and from the murex, a kind of sea snail in nearby waters, they extracted a brilliant purple dye. Due to its rarity and expense, this dye became the color of royalty throughout the ancient world.

AMAZEing ART: Wonders of the Ancient World, by Chris Berg ◼ HarperCollins*Publishers*

Phoenician Sailing Ship
The Most Advanced Naval Vessel of its Time
The Mediterranean, First and Second Millennium B.C.

"As for Africa, we know it to be washed on all sides by the sea, except where it is attached to Asia. This discovery was first made by Necos, the Egyptian pharaoh, who sent to sea a number of ships manned by Phoenicians. The Phoenicians took their departure from Egypt . . . and sailed into the southern ocean. When autumn came, they went ashore, wherever they might happen to be, and having sown a tract of land with corn, waited until the grain was fit to cut. Having reaped it, they again set sail; and thus it came to pass that two whole years went by, and it was not till the third year that they . . . made good their voyage home."

—Herodotus, Greek historian, fifth century b.c.

From the cedar trees that carpeted nearby mountains—the same cedarwood that Wen-Amun came to purchase—Phoenician shipwrights built seaworthy sailing ships to transport their glasswork, dyes, and other goods to Egypt, Greece, Anatolia, and the Aegean. Along their way they founded trading camps and developed sheltered harbors, and over time these grew into independent towns and cities. By the eighth century b.c. the Phoenician home cities of Tyre and Sidon were the hub of a commercial network that spanned the Mediterranean.

Phoenician sailors journeyed to the limits of the known world in search of markets and raw materials. A Phoenician from Carthage by the name of Hanno sailed down the coast of West Africa, where he saw rivers infested with crocodiles and hippopotamuses, was terrified by nocturnal drumming in the jungle, and skirmished with a group of "wild people with hairy bodies" that his guide called Gorillas. In a three-year voyage, Phoenicians in the service of Pharaoh Necho of Egypt (610–595 b.c.) probably even sailed all the way around Africa—two thousand years before Vasco da Gama, the Portuguese navigator who is usually given credit for this difficult feat, was even born. We can only guess at the appearance of the ships that accomplished these feats of exploration, for no complete Phoenician shipwreck has yet been found.

Most people who have heard of the Phoenicians have also heard that they invented the alphabet. This has been a common belief since ancient times, but it is not quite true. The Egyptians were actually the first to develop the beginnings of an alphabetic script, although they had little awareness of the value of their invention and largely ignored it. But the Egyptians may have passed the idea on to their neighbors in Syria and Palestine, some of whom later developed into the seafaring Phoenicians. Phoenician merchants then passed the alphabet on to the Greeks, who mistakenly gave them the credit for its invention.

THE MIGHT OF ASSYRIA

One day in 674 B.C. Esarhaddon, a powerful and capable ruler of Assyria, abdicated his responsibilities as king. He cast off his regal attire and traveled secretly far out into the countryside; there he hid, in fear for his life, on an obscure plot of farmland, tilling the soil like a common laborer. Only a select few from his inner circle of advisers and priests knew of his whereabouts, and if they dared write to him, they addressed their letters simply to "the Farmer." Like Esarhaddon himself, they too were afraid for the king's life, because only a few days before his abdication, one of the most ominous events imaginable had occurred—a total eclipse of the moon. To the Assyrians, this meant nothing less than the certain death of their king.

To counteract the prediction of his own death, Esarhaddon knew that a king of Assyria must die. So while he hid on a farm in the bizarre effort to conceal his identity from the gods, his priests and advisers did the only thing that would fulfill the omen: They swore in a common farmer as king. This substitute king was forced to "recite the scribal recitations before the Sun-god" and take all the celestial and terrestrial omens upon himself, and for a brief time he sat on the throne of Assyria, ruling over all its territories. Inevitably, however, the priests ensured that he "went to his destiny," after which Esarhaddon returned to the throne, resuming his rule over one of the most militaristic peoples known to history.

From their origins in a few major cities on the Tigris River in Northern Iraq—Nineveh, Ashur, and Kalakh—the Assyrians grew by the ninth century B.C. to control most of the Middle East, from Egypt to the Persian Gulf. They regarded warfare as their most important activity, and considered it a divinely inspired goal to impose their gods upon conquered territories. The Assyrians were the first major power to equip soldiers with iron weapons and to master the tactics of the light horse-drawn chariot, and this, combined with their superb military organization and cruel treatment of their enemies, turned them into the most successful fighting power the ancient world had yet seen. At its height the Assyrian army numbered in the hundreds of thousands, and the thunder of its chariots inspired terror in all who heard it.

The Assyrian strategy for conquest depended heavily on psychological warfare. They would first send their "cup-bearers"—the representatives of the king—to

"The city and its houses, from the foundations to its parapets, I destroyed, I razed, and I burned with fire. The city wall and outer wall, the temples, the temple tower, the bricks and dirt, I tore up . . . In the midst of that city I dug canals and flooded that area with water. I brought on it destruction greater than the Deluge . . . changing it into swamp."

—INSCRIPTION OF KING SENNACHERIB OF ASSYRIA RELATING HIS DESTRUCTION OF BABYLON IN 689 B.C.

47

Winged Guardian Bull (Lamassu)

From the Palace of Ashurnasirpal II, King of Assyria
Nimrud, Iraq, Ninth Century B.C.

S   E

AMAZEing ART: Wonders of the Ancient World, by Chris Berg ■ HarperCollins*Publishers*

try and persuade a city to surrender without a fight. If this failed, the Assyrian army would then surround the city and shout at the defenders, trying to convince them that resistance was useless. Woe to the people who still refused to capitulate, for if the Assyrians were forced to fight, they would then bring out their giant wheeled siege towers and enormous armored battering rams to breach the city walls. Once inside, Assyrian soldiers committed unspeakable atrocities upon the population before deporting the survivors for use as slave labor. This strategy was designed to intimidate nearby cities into surrendering without a fight and agreeing to pay an oppressive yearly tribute—and it usually worked. In their early artwork and inscriptions, the Assyrians boasted of this cruel and barbarous treatment of all who resisted them.

Deeply superstitious, Assyrian kings would not take any major military actions without first consulting their diviners. In addition to submitting detailed reports of their military campaigns to a statue of their supreme god, Assur, they also had many strange taboos. Sometimes they had to fast until a new moon appeared, sit inside a reed hut being treated as if they were ill, or even wear the clothes of a nanny. One of the Assyrian kings, Assurbanipal, who was a great patron of the arts, apparently got a little carried away with this, for he also wore cosmetics and spoke in a falsetto voice. This may have been too confusing for his soldiers, and it seems that one of his generals killed him while he was applying cosmetics.

After terrorizing their neighbors for centuries, the Assyrians were finally overcome by a coalition of the Babylonians and Medes, who laid waste to the Assyrian cities in 609 B.C. The many magnificent colossal statues of protective genies that had guarded the mighty Assyrian royal palaces, such as the human-headed bull pictured here, did nothing to interfere. Carved out of the rock by slaves taken during Assyria's many military campaigns, they looked silently out upon the burning cities with enigmatic smiles.

"I am powerful, I am omnipotent, I am a hero, I am gigantic, I am colossal!"

—PREAMBLE TO ONE OF KING ESARHADDON'S INSCRIPTIONS, SEVENTH CENTURY B.C.

"The fortunate people from all the lands, together with the people of Kalakh, have I entertained in splendor ten days, refreshed with wine, bathed, anointed, and heaped with every honor. Then I allowed them to depart in good spirits."

—INSCRIPTION OF KING ASHURNASIRPAL II OF ASSYRIA (883–859 B.C.), WHO ENTERTAINED 69,574 GUESTS FROM ALL PARTS OF HIS EMPIRE FOR TEN DAYS AT THE ROYAL PALACE AT NIMRUD

THE GARDENS
WITHOUT RIVAL

Everyone has heard of the famed "Hanging Gardens of Babylon." The name of this Wonder of the Ancient World conjures up visions of thick tangles of hanging vines and exotic flowered plants, suspended overhead by various devices, and hints at the decadence and greatness that once was Babylon. The most mysterious of the Wonders, the Hanging Gardens have captivated the imagination of artists and poets ever since Greek soldiers under Alexander the Great first returned from the Near East bringing tales of their magnificence and splendor.

The Hanging Gardens were described in detail by five classical authors, all of whom lived after the third century B.C. Planted with "all manner of trees," they were 400 feet square and rose to a height of about 80 feet. They sloped like a hillside, and "the several parts of the structure rose from one another tier on tier, the appearance of the whole resembling that of a theater." The plants did not actually hang, in the sense that foliage hung below their roots; this is a mistranslation of the original descriptions. Rather, the plants and trees were "up in the air" on artificial terraces, which were supported by great vaults that had been roofed over with stone slabs on which the soil and plants rested. Water was provided by machines hidden beneath the terraces; one author wrote with admiration that these were "screws, through which the water was continually conducted up into the garden" from the river below. The gardens were popularly attributed to the Babylonian King Nebuchadnezzar II of the sixth century B.C., who supposedly created them to console one of his wives who missed the mountains and greenery of her homeland.

Inspired by these vivid accounts, archaeologists have searched for the gardens among the ruins of Babylon for nearly a century, yet have come up with little more than vague conjectures as to their location. Babylonian kings, including Nebuchadnezzar, recorded elaborate inscriptions boasting of all their building programs, yet none of these make any references to gardens. Nor do a series of five cuneiform tablets known as the "Topography of Babylon," which list the city's temples, palaces, gates, and streets in great detail. Herodotus described the city in the fifth century B.C., and he too makes no mention of any gardens. The closer in time we

The Hanging Gardens
One of the Wonders of the Ancient World
Northern Iraq, Seventh Century B.C.
(BASED ON AN ASSYRIAN RELIEF SCULPTURE FROM 645 B.C. DEPICTING ROYAL GARDENS.)

AMAZEING ART: Wonders of the Ancient World, by Chris Berg ❖ HarperCollinsPublishers

"And then there were the Hanging Gardens—Paradeisos. Going up to the top is like climbing a mountain. Each terrace rises up from the last . . . it was flanked by perfectly constructed walls 25 feet thick. The galleries were roofed with stone balconies . . . the earth was deep enough to contain the roots of the many varieties of trees which fascinated the beholder with their great size and beauty. There was also a passage which had pipes leading up to the highest level and machinery to raise the water, through which great quantities of water were drawn from the river, with none of the process being visible from the outside."

—DIODORUS SICULUS, GREEK HISTORIAN, FIRST CENTURY B.C.

move to the fabled Hanging Gardens, the less evidence there is for their existence in Babylon.

This dearth of evidence has caused many to consider the later accounts of classical authors to be legends. Much more likely, however, is the recent well-argued suggestion that the "Hanging Gardens of Babylon," the most enchanting wonder of the ancient world, were never actually built in Babylon—but rather in Nineveh, the ancient city that was the heart of the militaristic Assyrian Empire.

The evidence supporting this is compelling. Jewish and Greek historians from antiquity have often confused Babylon and Nineveh, and ancient astronomical observations used by Johannes Kepler—purportedly originating from Babylon—have been proven to be from Nineveh. Details from the accounts of the gardens by classical authors, such as their descriptions of the artwork and geography of the city, fit Nineveh better than Babylon. And, most intriguingly, in the seventh century B.C. there was a fabulous garden built at Nineveh by the Assyrian king Sennacherib, whom ancient authors occasionally confused with Nebuchadnezzar; this garden was physically constructed by Babylonians who had been enslaved by Sennacherib.

Sennacherib was known to have been personally interested in botany, and his gardens, which were laid out like the slope of a great mountain, were stocked with rare and exotic plants, herbs, and trees from far-flung lands. To water them, the king had a 30-mile network of canals and aqueducts constructed, and boasted in an inscription that a form of screw was used to raise the water up to the level of the highest plants. The gardens were only a small part of Sennacherib's vast palace, which was half a kilometer long and of unparalleled splendor. Called Shanina-la-ishu, meaning "Nonesuch" or "the Palace Without Rival," its imposing facade towered 65 feet above 80-foot-high city walls, and its hundreds of rooms and courtyards were lined with over two miles of superbly carved relief sculptures and at least 120 colossal figures of human-headed winged bulls. It was everywhere decorated with gold, ivory, and precious aromatic woods, the gifts and treasures from subject nations all across the Near East. Sennacherib's palace gardens—almost certainly the true Wonder of the Ancient World—could thus be called "the Terraced Gardens of Nineveh," or better yet, "the Gardens Without Rival."

"Time destroys, by insensible corrosion, not only human works, but even nature herself; yet this pile, pressed with the roots and loaded with the trunks of so gigantic a plantation, still remains entire."

—QUINTUS CURTIUS, ROMAN RHETORICIAN, *History of Alexander*, FIRST CENTURY A.D.

THE ANCIENT TOWER
OF BABEL

Whatever language we speak and whatever culture we are from, most of us have heard of the legendary Tower of Babel. As told in the Book of Genesis, this mighty structure that reached into the heavens was built in the land of "Shinar" after the Deluge. Its builders sought to immortalize themselves, but God, recognizing their vanity, disrupted their work by confusing the speech of the workers so that they could no longer understand one another. The tower was never completed, and the people were scattered over the face of the earth.

The myth of the Tower of Babel was almost certainly inspired by the ancient Ziggurat of Marduk at Babylon, an enormous seven-stage multicolored pyramidal tower that was over 300 feet in height. In the Akkadian language, Babylon was written "Bab-ili," meaning "Gate of the Gods." The similarity of this word to the Hebrew word *balal* ("to confuse") led to a play on words in Genesis: "Therefore its name was called Babel, because there the Lord confounded (*balal*) the language of all the earth." The ziggurat was first constructed by Hammurabi as early as the eighteenth century B.C., and was enlarged by later kings including Nebuchadnezzar II, the ruler despised by the Hebrews for sacking their cities and bringing many of their people in captivity to Babylon.

The ziggurat was made entirely of brick, and was topped by a glazed blue temple to the god Marduk, the Babylonian deity who represented order and battled against the powers of chaos. The Babylonians' name for the tower was Etemenanki, meaning "Foundation of Heaven and Earth," and it was so revered that during one of its many rebuildings a Babylonian king had his sons haul bricks like common laborers to show their piety. From its peak, priests burned great quantities of frankincense, which wafted up to the heavens to please the gods. From atop the tower, astronomer-priests also made precise observations of Marduk (the planet Jupiter) as he crossed the night sky, for they believed that the movements of heavenly bodies controlled the lives of men. These early observations formed the beginnings of both astrology and astronomy.

"On the summit of the tower, there is a spacious shrine, inside which there stands a couch of unusual size, richly adorned, with a golden table by its side. No statue of any kind is erected there, and no one occupies the room at night except a single woman whom the god, so the priests say, has especially chosen for himself. They also say that the god comes to the room in person and sleeps on the bed. I do not believe it myself."

—HERODOTUS, GREEK HISTORIAN, FIFTH CENTURY B.C., DESCRIBING THE ZIGGURAT OF MARDUK

53

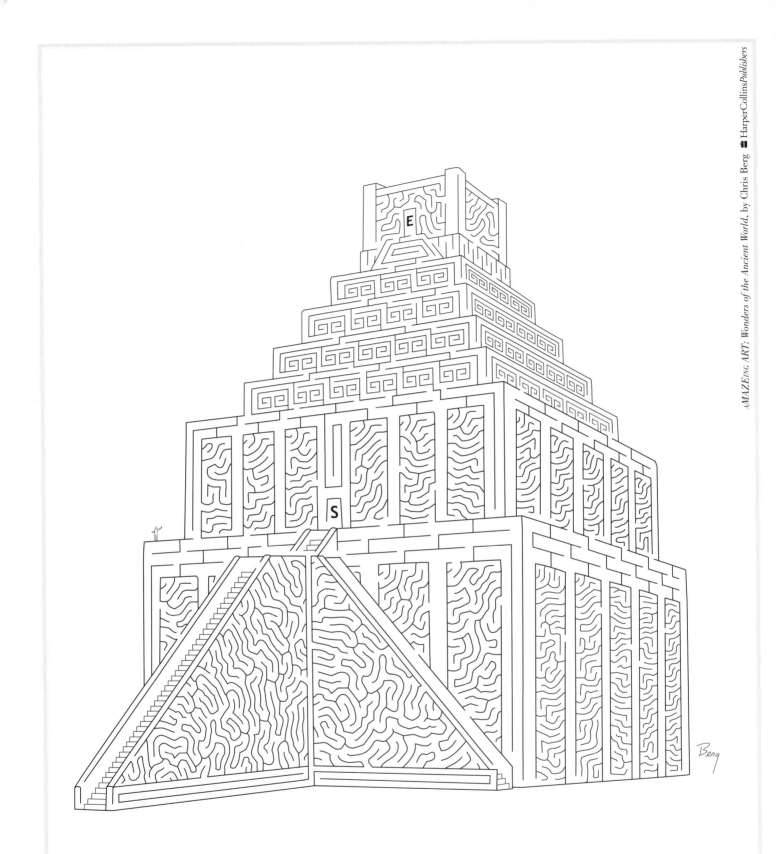

The Ziggurat of Marduk at Babylon
The Biblical Tower of Babel
Babylon, Iraq, Seventh Century B.C.

When Babylon was at its height under King Nebuchadnezzar in the sixth century B.C., it surpassed in splendor any city in the known world and was the preeminent religious and cultural center of the Ancient Near East. Its wide streets, many of which were paved and intersected each other at right angles, teemed with a confusing jumble of people speaking languages from the farthest corners of the earth. Merchants from Egypt, Iran, Syria, Palestine, and Asia Minor all journeyed to this ancient metropolis on the Euphrates River to market their goods, mingling with priests and moneylenders. Commerce centered around the city's many temples, which functioned much like modern banks, lending out money to farmers, businessmen, and speculators at a high rate of interest, usually 20 percent. As repayment for the loans, the temple priests received all manner of goods, from barley beer and livestock to gold and spices, which they sold right back to the public at the crowded temple markets.

According to Herodotus, the Babylonians clothed themselves in linen tunics reaching to their feet, wore turbans on their heads, and anointed their entire bodies with perfumes daily. In addition to a walking-stick, which was always intricately carved, men carried a seal stone by which they identified themselves and signed clay documents. In an interesting custom, when a Babylonian became ill he was laid out in the public square, and passersby were required to come up and ask him about his illness. Everyone who had ever had this disease then gave the sick person advice, recommending whatever had worked in their own cases. The Babylonians also had capable doctors, which may have been because of the punishments for medical malpractice; these included removing the eye of a doctor who had, through negligence, blinded a patient.

Time has not spared Babylon, and today the site is little more than a few desolate mounds of cracked earth jutting out of the desert sand. Ironically the Ziggurat of Marduk, which Nebuchadnezzar had faced with a 15-meter-thick layer of the finest burnt bricks so that it might last for millennia, is among the most poorly preserved of ruins. Nebuchadnezzar's bricks—which still bear his mark—were so well-made that locals plundered the ruins of the ziggurat looking for them, and thus hardly even its foundations remain.

"If a builder makes a house for a man and does not make its construction firm, and the house which he has built [should] collapse and cause the death of the owner of the house … that builder shall be put to death."

—HAMURRABI OF BABYLON, *Code of Laws*, TWENTY-THIRD CENTURY B.C.

"This is the ancient Babel, and now lies in ruins; but the streets still extend thirty miles. The ruins of the Palace of Nebuchadnezzar are still to be seen; but people are afraid to venture among them on account of the serpents and scorpions with which they are infested."

—BENJAMIN OF TUDELA, RABBI AND TRAVELER, ELEVENTH CENTURY A.D.

KING XERXES'S DREAM

The Achaemenid Persians were a group of seminomadic tribesmen who, through superior military tactics and astute diplomacy, managed to conquer much of the civilized world in the Near East in an astonishingly brief 25-year period, founding the Persian Empire in the sixth century B.C. Early Persian kings ruled with creative tolerance over vast and diverse territories, but later rulers became despotic. In one of history's momentous turning points, one of these later kings, Xerxes, led an enormous invasion army against the Greeks in an attempt to further expand his domain.

Xerxes had spent four years gathering his army from all corners of the Persian empire, and among its roughly 200,000 men were Persian knights in armor, Ethiopian warriors in leopard skins, and Indians in cotton dresses. The most renowned contingent were the so-called Immortals, 10,000 of the most valiant Persian fighters who were bedecked in precious gold and accompanied by their own handsomely dressed attendants and concubines.

Supported by a myriad of servants and beasts of burden, Xerxes's host rode forth in the spring of 480 B.C. The army was so large that it literally drank small rivers dry, and cities along its route were impoverished by their efforts to provide a single sumptuous dinner banquet for Xerxes and the Immortals. Two great bridges, made of hundreds of boats lashed together with one-foot-thick Egyptian papyrus cables, were built for the army to cross from Asia to Europe over the Hellespont. When these were blown away in a gale, Xerxes in his anger had the engineers beheaded, and allegedly ordered that the sea itself be flogged and admonished with these words: "Thou bitter water, thy lord lays on thee this punishment because thou hast wronged him without a cause!" When the bridges were rebuilt, Xerxes was so confident of his impending victory that he allowed Greek grain ships bound for Athens to pass through them, reputedly saying, "We too are bound thither. What harm is it, if they carry our provisions for us?" Later, when three Greek spies were caught trying to observe his army, he even ordered that they be given a grand tour and allowed to depart—reasoning that if the Greeks became aware of the immensity of his forces, they would surrender.

The Greeks, however, did not surrender. The Persian army initially beat down their every attempt at resistance, and the Athenians were forced to abandon

Ruins of the Gate of Xerxes

Persepolis, Capital of the Persian Empire

Iran, Fifth Century B.C.

AMAZEing ART: Wonders of the Ancient World, by Chris Berg ✚ HarperCollinsPublishers

Athens, fleeing in disarray to the nearby island of Salamis. From there they saw the reddish glow of their city as it burned at night, and were distraught by the frightful beauty of the enormous spark-clouds that rose up to the heavens, seeming to seal their doom. Yet there at Salamis the 370 ships of the Greek navy made a final stand, and in the narrow straits managed to defeat the larger fleet of the Persians. With its navy routed, Xerxes's enormous army lacked a secure source of supply and had to postpone further offensive actions—which ultimately led to its defeat.

After his defeat Xerxes returned to Persia, where he spent much of his Empire's remaining wealth on a vast building program. Persepolis was one of his major projects. It was not a city in the usual sense but rather a large complex of splendid palaces, treasuries, and audience halls standing on a wide platform of natural rock, with entrance gates guarded by winged demons and human-headed bulls. The Greeks would have their revenge against the Persians in 330 B.C. when Alexander the Great, after defeating the Persian armies, burned Persepolis to the ground during a night of drunken revels. Whether this was a deliberate act or an accident we shall probably never know, but ironically it preserved the ruins in excellent condition for archaeologists.

As some historians have observed, the Greek fleet at Salamis was able to best the Persians partly because two unusual storms had passed through the Aegean Sea a few weeks before the battle, miraculously wrecking around 600 Persian ships. If it were not for these storms the Greeks would surely have been defeated and conquered by Xerxes. There would have been no flowering of Greek democracy at Athens in the fifth century B.C.—no Parthenon, no Socrates, no Plato, no Aristotle. Today our children might be learning, in some Indo-Iranian language, that the cultural achievements of ancient Persian nomadic tribesmen are "the bedrock of our civilization," and that the Greeks, well, they were a minor people who disappeared from history without achieving very much. All possible, perhaps, but for two rogue storms in the late summer of 480 B.C.

"They thanked the gods very warmly, in that they had caused Xerxes to be content with only one meal in the day. For had the order been to provide breakfast for the king's host as well as dinner, the Abderites must either have fled before Xerxes came, or, if they awaited his coming, have been brought to absolute ruin."

—HERODOTUS, GREEK HISTORIAN, FIFTH CENTURY B.C.

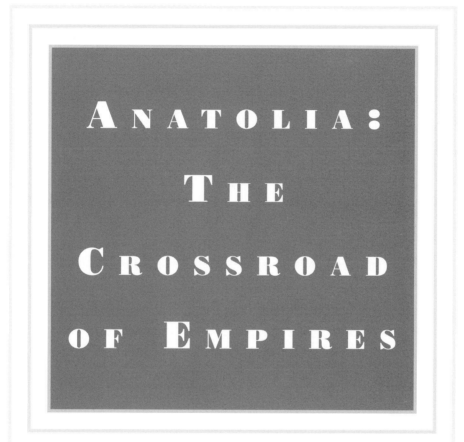

THE LOST EMPIRE
OF THE HITTITES

In 1323 B.C. the aged Hittite king, Shuppiluliuma I, after 25 years of arduous campaigning, was finally encamped by the great Syrian fortress-city of Carcemish with little to do but enjoy his sleep. Carcemish had just surrendered to the Hittite armies after an eight-day siege, and aside from providing his troops with some much-needed rest, the city's fall meant that Shuppiluliuma now controlled a defensible buffer state in northern Syria, a rich area that the Egyptians and Assyrians both coveted.

So when a messenger arrived carrying a diplomatic letter from Egypt, Shuppiluliuma was prepared for the worst: threats, demands, or ultimatums. As the message was read, however, the King could not contain his astonishment, and at first thought someone was playing a joke on him. It was from the young Queen of Egypt, Ankhesenamun, wife of the boy-king Tutankhamun, and it said: "My husband has died, and I have no son, but of you it is said you have many sons. If you would send me one of your sons, he could become my husband. I will on no account take one of my subjects and make him my husband. I am very much afraid." As Shuppiluliuma well knew, whoever married Ankhesenamun would become ruler of Egypt. It was a glittering prize—the land of the pharaohs in all its length and breadth—that the young queen was offering.

Ankhesenamun's offer is preserved on a clay tablet from the temple archives at Khattusha, the ancient capital of the Hittite empire, and it reveals that the Hittites, who were virtually unknown to historians until about a century ago, were once one of the greatest imperial powers of the ancient Near East. A rugged people whose homeland, Hatti, was a mountainous plateau in Anatolia, they were skilled in mountain warfare and feared for their chariotry; a Hittite King, Murshili I, once conquered Babylon and put an end to Hammaurabi's dynasty. Hittite kings possessed near-absolute power, combining the duties of chief priest, head of the armed forces, and chief judge and lawgiver; one of their laws reads, "If anyone rejects the ruling of the king, his house shall be made a heap of ruins." Yet they also had a preoccupation with literature, filling the libraries of their capital city with mythical works written in many different languages; they were also fascinated with history, often including long his-

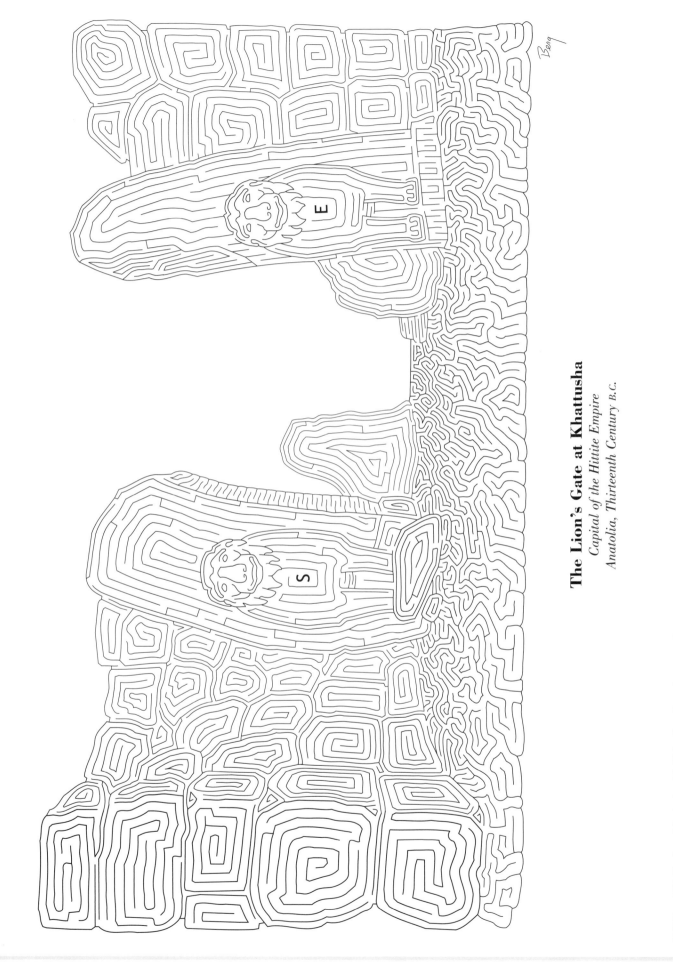

The Lion's Gate at Khattusha
Capital of the Hittite Empire
Anatolia, Thirteenth Century B.C.

"Furthermore, if people are dying for some other reason, let me see it in a dream, or let it be determined by an oracle. Or in respect to what I command of all the priests—let them sleep on a pure bed... may the gods, my lords, manifest their providence, and may someone see it in a dream. And may the reason that people are dying be discovered."

—THE PLAGUE PRAYER OF THE HITTITE KING MURSHILI II, FOURTEENTH CENTURY B.C.

torical preambles in their diplomatic treaties. Unlike in other civilizations of the age, Hittite queens possessed real authority and conducted important official correspondence with foreign states. They were a complex and vibrant people.

The Hittites worshipped nearly a thousand gods, all ruled by the great storm-god Teshup, who was often shown standing alone and grasping a symbolic lightning bolt and an ax. They kept solid silver statues of these gods within their many temples, and gave them food and drink, changes of clothing, and live shows—including music, acrobatics, and sword-swallowing demonstrations—to keep them entertained. The Hittites learned the will of their gods in dreams, and slept on "pure beds" in sacred temples in the hopes of receiving a dream oracle, which would then be interpreted by knowledgeable seers. The King was himself considered semi-divine, and was carefully guarded from any sources of impurity in his food and clothing that might damage his sacred powers.

The ending of the story of King Shuppiluliuma, like that of the Hittites themselves, is tragic. Shuppiluliuma hesitated and when he finally did send one of his sons, powerful forces within the Egyptian military conspired to assassinate him before he could reach the frightened queen. As for the Hittites, a great movement of peoples known as the Sea Peoples, whose superiority was due largely to the use of iron weapons, overwhelmed their empire in the thirteenth century B.C. A major drought and climate change throughout the Mediterranean may have been behind this migration. The very existence of the Hittites was soon forgotten, and the sprawling ruins of Khattusha, the "City of a Thousand Gods," with its impressive citadel, many temples, and massive cyclopean walls, is one of the few tangible remains of their lost empire.

TROY,

"WHERE NO STONE

IS NAMELESS"

Troy and its legendary war have captivated people in the West for nearly three thousand years. The story has its beginnings in the dark ages before Homer, when Greek bards chanted epic tales of valiant heroes and beautiful women, distant lands, and the vengeance of the gods. The basic story, as told in Homer's *Iliad* and other tales, concerns a great Greek expedition launched against Troy to recover the beautiful Helen, who has been abducted by Paris, the Trojan prince. After a ten-year siege during which many heroes, including Achilles, are killed, the Greeks finally capture and sack the city of Troy by tricking the defenders into accepting an enormous wooden horse that concealed Greek soldiers. After their victory the Greeks depart, but are delayed and punished by the gods during their voyage home.

In the ancient world there was an almost uniform belief that the Trojan War was an historical event, and a whole series of conquerors, from Xerxes to Julius Caesar, visited the city of Troy to pay homage to the shades of Homer's heroes. Alexander the Great traced his lineage to Achilles and slept with an annotated copy of the *Iliad* next to his dagger, and when he came to Troy he anointed his body with oil and ran naked to Achilles's tomb. There he was said to have remarked that Achilles was "a lucky man, in that he had Homer to proclaim his deeds and preserve his memory." Roman emperors, too, often traced their lineage to the Trojans. Caesar wandered about looking for the remains of a great citadel; he found little but overgrown trees, yet was inspired by the sight of the plains "where so many heroes died, where no stone is nameless." The strangest story of all concerns Emperor Caracalla, who we are told paid his respects to Achilles by cremating his own friend Festus—who was alive—in order to reenact Achilles's mourning of Patroclus.

In medieval times many nations, in order to make themselves appear to be a noble people guided by the gods toward a splendid destiny, obsessively tried to establish their descent from the Trojans. The most popular of such attempts was the twelfth-century bestseller *The History of the Kings of Britain*, by Geoffrey of

"Anyone who doesn't think the Trojans were utterly stupid will have realized that the horse was really an engineer's device for breaking down the walls."

—PAUSANIAS, GREEK TRAVEL WRITER, SECOND CENTURY A.D.

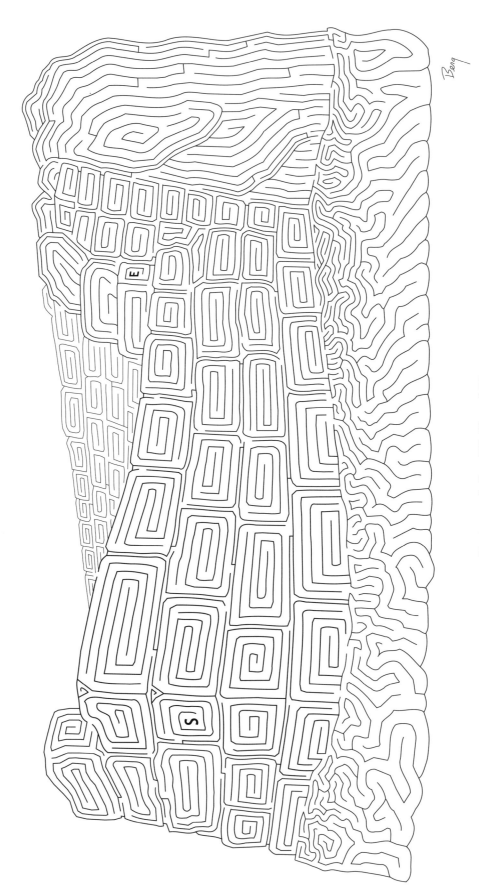

Ruins of the Walls of Troy
Legendary Bronze Age Citadel
Anatolia, Thirteenth Century B.C.

Monmouth. Geoffrey invented a hero named Brutus, supposedly descended from Aeneas, who fled Rome for Britain with the last of the Trojans and founded London as "New Troy." Although more level-headed medieval historians dismissed it as a "tissue of absurdities," Geoffrey's work was admired for many centuries, and Tudor kings themselves embraced the Trojans as their ancestors. The early turf labyrinths, often called "the Walls of Troy," that can be found throughout England and Wales are distant reminders of this belief.

The famed archaeologist Heinrich Schliemann is often given credit for the modern rediscovery of Troy in 1870. Actually, the first person to correctly identify the city was the Scotsman Charles Maclaren in 1822, and a British archaeologist, Frank Calvert, was the first to excavate the site. Schliemann, a "round-headed, round-faced, round-hatted, great round goggle-eyed" man, was a self-made millionaire who spoke ten languages and knew how to market himself to the public. His general approach was to offer knowledgeable archaeologists generous salaries to work under him, and then hire journalists to write articles about himself and his discoveries.

Schliemann was also a pathological liar and a fraud. His discovery of "Priam's Treasure" at Troy, which came within weeks of severe criticism of his methods and conclusions, has been proven to have been faked—several pieces of the treasure were discovered in photos from years earlier. In Schliemann's own account of the find, he dismissed all his workmen and dug alone, with only his dear wife to help him wrap the golden jewelry in her shawl; unfortunately for Schliemann, his dear wife was actually in Athens at the time. Many of his critical personal diary entries and letters relating to the early excavations have also been shown to have been forged, altered, or backdated. In his quest for glory, Schliemann dug vast trenches and demolished everything in his way, including the real walls of Homer's Troy, which, not recognizing them, he dug right through and partially destroyed.

Later archaeologists uncovered fascinating clues at Troy hinting at the historical basis of the Trojan War. The fortifications at the site are impressive, with a pronounced slant and one inferior section of the wall "where the city is easiest to attack"—all exactly as described by Homer. And the city, which had rich deposits of Mycenaean (Greek) potsherds, was destroyed at just about the time the Trojan War might have occurred. If Caesar's stones could only speak, we might marvel at the tales they could tell.

"Troy was for a considerable period to the Heathen world, what Jerusalem is now to the Christian, a 'sacred' city which attracted pilgrims by the fame of its wars and its woes, and by the shadow of the ancient sanctity reposing upon it. Without abusing language, we may say that a voice speaking from this hill, three thousand years ago sent its utterance over the whole ancient world, as its echoes still reverberate over the modern."

—CHARLES MACLAREN, ANTIQUARIAN, *The Plain of Troy Described* (1863)

GREECE AND THE AGE OF HEROES

THE LABYRINTH
AND THE MINOTAUR

In 1894 the English archaeologist Arthur Evans, while perusing the offerings of antiquities dealers in the Athens flea market, noticed some peculiar symbols etched on tiny seal stones. Evans was told the stones came from the mountainous island of Crete, and, fascinated by their strange appearance, he used his own money to buy a plot of land on the island at Knossos. This site had long been suspected of harboring ancient ruins, and when Evans began full-scale excavations there he soon uncovered the labyrinthine foundations of an elegant Bronze Age palace, the remains of an extraordinary lost civilization. He chose to name this civilization Minoan after a legendary king named Minos, who according to Greek tradition had once ruled over a great sea-empire from Crete.

The Minoans flourished during the middle of the second millennium B.C., building mysterious cave and mountaintop sanctuaries, luxurious villas, and remarkably elegant palaces all across their island. They developed extended trading links, grew rich from seaborne commerce with the Egyptians and Greeks, and used an early form of writing now known as Linear A, which has yet to be deciphered. At the height of the empire, Minoan towns, ports, roads, and fortification walls dotted the rugged Cretan landscape, and Minoan settlements and trading colonies could be found throughout the Mediterranean.

Knossos is the largest of the Minoan palaces, and like others it is an agglomeration of rooms clustered around a long, rectangular central court. Only the ruins of its foundations have survived, but these reveal a vast interconnected complex of small corridors, staircases, and private rooms containing residential quarters, workshops, administrative areas, and many different cult centers. Stairways led to large upper rooms made of wood that have not survived, but which probably rose five stories in height. An elaborate and advanced system of drains, conduits, and terra-cotta pipes provided water and sanitation, and deep courtyards known as light-wells created an airy and comfortable atmosphere. Palace walls were decorated with delicate and vibrant frescoes depicting scenes of lithe young athletes leaping over bulls, ladies gossiping and dancing, and dolphins and other animals in magical gardens, all done

"Minos resolved to banish his shame from the house and to close it up in a sinister edifice with many chambers. Daedalus created the work, and he fitted out its chambers with deceptive signs; into the windings of the tangling passages he misled the eye."

—OVID, ROMAN POET, FIRST CENTURY B.C.

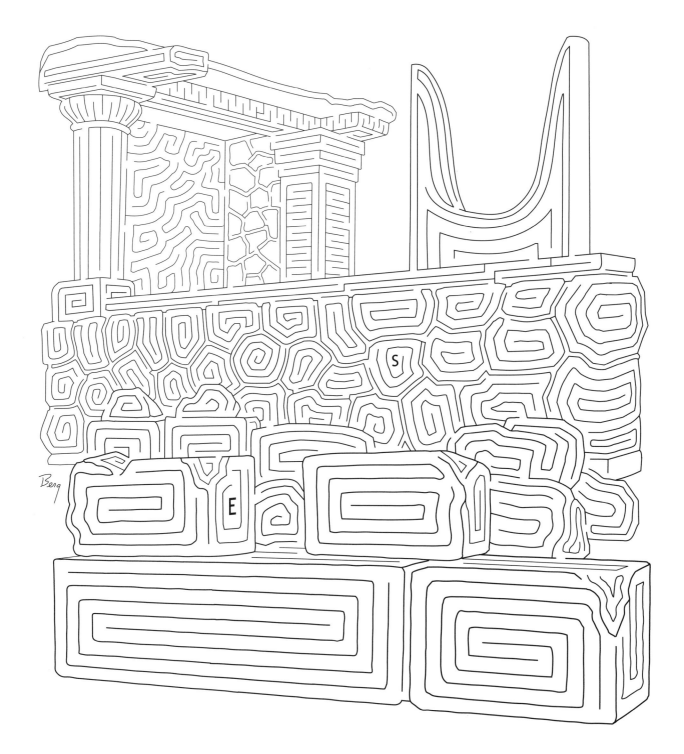

The Palace at Knossos
Splendid Ruin of Minoan Civilization
Crete, 2000 to 1400 B.C.

AMAZEing ART: Wonders of the Ancient World, by Chris Berg ▪ HarperCollins*Publishers*

in a naturalistic style that emphasized movement and grace. The palace's interior floors were covered with crystalline white gypsum, and its outer facade was rendered in strikingly varied color and crowned with many bull horns, a sacred symbol that the Minoans may have worshipped.

The palace at Knossos consisted of perhaps 1,300 rooms spread over three acres of land. Since its discovery, many have speculated that this complex structure, with its ever-present bull symbolism, was the distant inspiration behind the labyrinth in the Greek myth of Theseus and the Minotaur. In this myth, an ingenious labyrinth was built to contain the half-man, half-bull Minotaur to which the Cretans sacrificed Athenian children. Recent discoveries of the bones of four young children in a house outside the palace, found mixed in with the remains of edible snails and animal bones, only strengthen the parallels.

Over the centuries the Minoan palaces weathered many destructions and disasters, including the catastrophic volcanic explosion of the nearby island of Thera (now Santorini) in 1628 B.C. This cataclysmic eruption was about 75,000 times more powerful than the earliest atomic bombs, and could probably have been heard as far away as Norway. The great volumes of volcanic ash it spewed into the atmosphere plunged the entire globe into a "nuclear winter" for many years; chroniclers in China at this time reported a "yellow fog, dim sun, frost in July, and famine." Knossos itself was shattered by a series of earthquakes that preceded or accompanied the eruption; and a 200-mile-per-hour tidal wave that was perhaps 50 feet high—a tsunami—leveled settlements along the northern coast of Crete. After the explosion, 30 square miles of land at the center of Thera collapsed into a hollow caldera and sank one thousand feet beneath the ocean, an event that may have given rise to Plato's legend of the lost continent of Atlantis.

Despite the violence of the eruption of Thera, Minoan civilization recovered and even prospered for nearly two more centuries, until around 1450 B.C. when Minoan palaces, towns, and country houses all across Crete were destroyed by fire, never to be rebuilt. The cause of this destruction is uncertain: It may have been due to Mycenaean invaders from mainland Greece, an internal revolt, or even another massive earthquake. Knossos itself survived until 1375 B.C., but then it too succumbed to destruction and was left in ruins. In the stonecutter's rooms in one corner of the palace, excavators uncovered scattered and half-finished stone utensils and tools, mute testimony to the suddenness of this final destruction.

"And Minos ordered [the Athenians] to send seven young men and the same number of girls without weapons to be fodder for the Minotaur. Now the Minotaur was confined in a labyrinth, in which he who entered could not find his way out; for many a winding turn shut off the secret outward way."

—APOLLODORUS, GREEK SCHOLAR AND WRITER, SECOND CENTURY B.C.

THE LORDS OF MYCENAE

The most illustrious piece of ox dung in the ancient world—a piece of dung that became famous in Homeric legend—was laid in the thirteenth century B.C. outside the city of Troy, during the Trojan War. The circumstances behind its fame involve the funeral games of Patroklos, a friend of the Greek hero Achilles who was killed during the fighting for Troy. Funeral games, in which well-born contestants vied in tests of strength and skill for the most valued possessions of a deceased warrior, were a common custom among the warlike Bronze Age Greeks, and would later evolve into more permanent festivals such as the Olympics. Patroklos's games included a chariot race, boxing and wrestling matches, an archery contest, combat in full armor, and—significantly for our piece of dung—a quarter-mile sprint race.

For the sprint race the winner's prize was a fine silver winebowl, crafted by Phoenician artisans, that had belonged to Patroklos. It could hold six gallons of wine, and there was "never a mixing bowl in all the world that could match its beauty." Three men stepped forward to vie for the bowl: the wily Odysseus, who would later build the Trojan horse; Aias, a warrior who was fleet of foot; and Antilokhos, the fastest of the younger men. As soon as the race began Aias quickly took the lead, though all the Greeks cheered for the much older Odysseus, the "great contender." Ever mindful of the gods, Odysseus, as he ran, uttered a small prayer of victory to the gray-eyed goddess Athena who watched over him. Athena heard his prayer, and as the runners neared the last hundred yards she caused Aias to slip and fall on a pile of ox dung, making Odysseus victorious. The crowd of Greek warriors, decked in their precious bronze armor and carrying great black bull-hide shields and long spears, laughed in glee as Aias spat dung out of his mouth and cursed his ill luck.

This amusing incident from Homer's *Iliad* vividly portrays the heroic era in which Greeks such as Achilles, Odysseus, and Aias lived. It was a time of gods and heroes, when hereditary princes, transported to the battlefield on costly chariots, contended with each other in single combat or in small groups to resolve their disputes. The era is known as the Mycenaean Age, after the name of a fortified city on mainland Greece that looms large in Greek myth and legend—Mycenae. Mycenaean princes were linked together by a loose network of feudal obligations supporting a king, who

Ruins of the Lion's Gate at Mycenae
Legendary City of King Agamemnon
Greece, Thirteenth Century B.C.

aMAZEing ART: Wonders of the Ancient World, by Chris Berg · HarperCollins*Publishers*

"Anger be now your song,

immortal one,

Achilles's anger, doomed

and ruinous,

that caused the Akhaians

loss on bitter loss

and crowded brave souls

into the undergloom

. . . and the will of Zeus was

done."

—OPENING LINES
TO HOMER'S *Iliad*,
NINTH CENTURY B.C.

was the "first among equals." From their huge estates in the fertile Greek valleys they became rich through trading olive oil and wine to rulers in Egypt and other foreign lands, receiving in exchange horses, silver, gold, and slaves. Their imposing walled fortresses, often placed at the summits of hills or rocky outcrops, were made of boulders so enormous that later generations of Greeks thought they had been built by mythical one-eyed giants they called the Cyclops.

Mycenae was the greatest of their citadels, celebrated by Homer as "broad-streeted" and "rich in gold." Its 30-foot-thick stone walls guarded the king's palace, which was a *megaron*—a large, squarish room with an anteroom and vestibule that contained a central hearth open to the sky. A great fire burning in this hearth illuminated smooth plastered floors and richly painted walls, decorated with colorful geometric patterns and hunting and battle scenes. Storage areas, an underground water supply, and the houses of lesser nobility were nearby. Entry to the citadel was through the monumental Lion's Gate in the outer wall, which was placed so that approaching attackers would have their right, or unshielded, side facing the defenders along the fortifications. The overall aura was of power.

Mycenaean civilization flourished for more than three centuries, only to come to an abrupt end in the twelfth century B.C. due to a series of natural disasters. Major earthquakes laid low the Mycenaean citadels, and a severe climate change caused prolonged draught and massive crop failures. Trade with foreign kingdoms withered and many Mycenaean towns and villages were completely abandoned. There were great migrations of peoples throughout the Mediterranean at this time, leading to the sudden destruction of several other empires, including the Hittites. One of the last clues we have to the fate of the Mycenaeans comes from the palace of Pylos, where a clay tablet was found that reads "the Watchers are guarding the coasts." Immediately after this comment was written down, the palace was burned to the ground by unknown forces, and a dark age lasting centuries fell upon Greece.

THE IMPERISHABLE GLORY

OF ATHENS

The Parthenon was the preeminent architectural symbol of Athens' cultural renaissance in the fifth century B.C., a brilliant and fertile epoch in human history. This small city of 30,000 citizens was home to such original minds as the playwrights Sophocles, Euripides, and Aristophanes; the philosophers Socrates, Plato, and Aristotle; Hippocrates, the father of medicine; and Herodotus, one of the first historians. We still conceive of the world today using terms that these men created.

Completed in 438 B.C. during the reign of the great statesman Pericles, the Parthenon rose from the destruction wrought by the invading Persians when they had sacked the city of Athens forty years earlier. Perched atop the Acropolis—a rocky outcrop in the middle of the city—the temple could be seen from many miles away by approaching travelers.

As the culmination of the development of the Doric order, the most austere of the three Greek architectural orders, the Parthenon embodied a striking number of architectural refinements. There is a barely perceptible rise in the center of its foundation, and its columns lean inward and have a slight swelling. The distance between columns varies, and the corner columns are slightly thickened. These subtle refinements combine to give the temple an organic, sculpted appearance, and the Athenians regarded it as their greatest artistic achievement.

The Parthenon was the abode of Athena, patron deity of the city of Athens, and housed a 39-foot statue of Athena sculpted by Phidias, a renowned Greek sculptor. It was said of Phidias that he alone had seen the true image of the gods, revealing it to humanity in his statues. Phidias's Athena stood erect, holding a great spear in her left hand and a goddess of victory (Nike) in her extended right hand. Her hands, feet, and face were all made of ivory, while her helmet, sandals, and dress were of gold. Her breastplate was emblazoned with an ivory medusa, her helmet was ornamented with an image of the sphinx. A decorated shield and a serpent lay by her side.

Athena's appearance is known only from literary references and a few surviving reproductions, for like all of Phidias's great statues it has not survived. It cost

"To dedicate those buildings [our forefathers] did not tithe themselves, nor fulfill the imprecations of their enemies by doubling the income tax. No, they conquered their enemies, they fulfilled the prayers of every sound-hearted man by establishing concord throughout the city, and so they have bequeathed to us their imperishable glory."

— DEMOSTHENES,
GREEK ORATOR,
FOURTH CENTURY B.C.

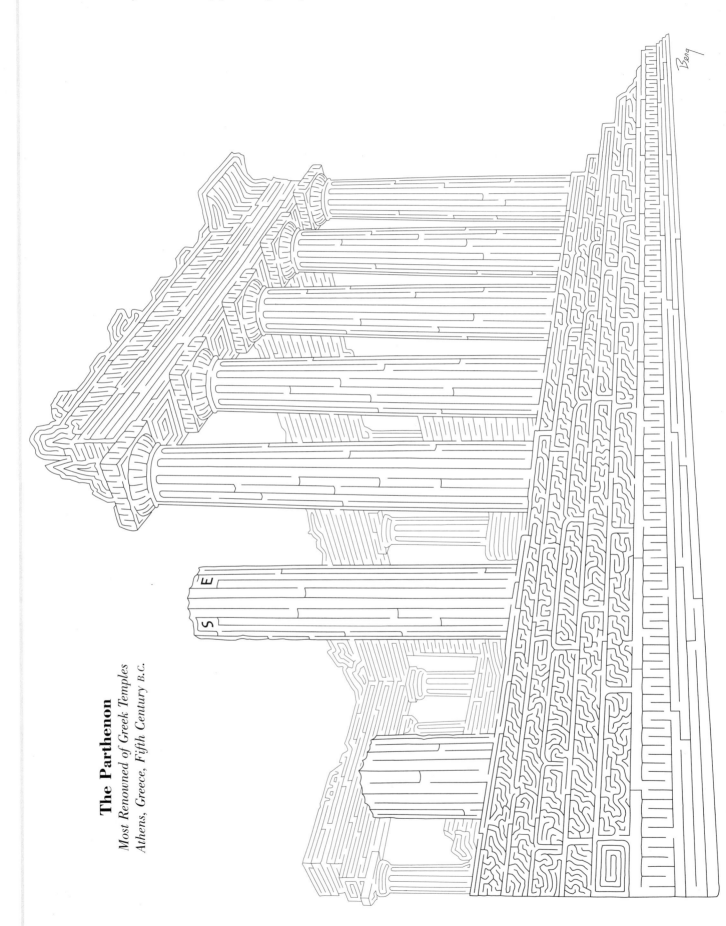

The Parthenon
Most Renowned of Greek Temples
Athens, Greece, Fifth Century B.C.

700 talents to build, which was enough money to build 300 warships. Controversy over this lavish expenditure, and a charge of impiety for including his own portrait among several dozen small figures on the statue's decorated shield, would force Phidias to flee Athens in fear for his life. He would later sculpt the famous Statue of Zeus at Olympia, one of the Seven Wonders of the Ancient World.

Aside from minor additions, such as a set of gilded shields donated by Alexander the Great, the Parthenon remained intact until the fifth century A.D. when it was converted into a Christian church. In 1460 the Turks turned it into a mosque and raised a minaret on one corner. Its appearance today is the result of a massive explosion that occurred during a bombardment of the Acropolis in 1687 by Venetians fighting the Turks. The Turkish army used the temple as a powder magazine, and a Venetian mortar found its mark. The resulting explosion destroyed much of the temple and cut the remaining ruins into two halves, scattering pieces of the entablature and columns all over the Acropolis. The most famous fragments of the ruined Parthenon did not remain long in Greece, for in the eighteenth century Lord Elgin removed most of the frieze, the sculpted stone metopes, and the pediment sculptures. Known as the Elgin Marbles, they now reside at the British Museum in London.

In ancient times the Parthenon was not plain white marble, for the temple was painted. There were dark blues for the ceiling and outer walls, a glowing burnished gold for the columns, and other hues for the details of the sculptures and ornamentation. Remains of these original paints can be found in tiny crevices and faults in the stone. What a sight the temple must have been, perched atop the hill of the Acropolis, its golden columns reflecting the last rays of the setting sun, its outer walls blending into the deepening blue of the evening sky.

"I never learned how to tune a harp, or play upon a lute; but I know how to raise a small and obscure city to glory and greatness . . . whereto all kindreds of the earth will pilgrim."

—THE GREEK ADMIRAL THEMISTOCLES, WHO DEFEATED THE PERSIANS AT THE BATTLE OF SALAMIS, ON BEING TAUNTED WITH HIS LACK OF SOCIAL SKILLS, FIFTH CENTURY B.C.

"And we shall assuredly not be without witnesses, for there are mighty monuments of our power which will make us the wonder of this and of succeeding ages; we shall not need the praises of Homer or of any other panegyrist whose poetry may please for the moment . . . For we have compelled every land and every sea to open a path for our valor, and have everywhere planted eternal memorials of our friendship and of our enmity. Such is the city for whose sake these men nobly fought and died."

—PERICLES, GREEK STATESMAN, FIFTH CENTURY B.C., *Funeral Oration*

ZEUS AND
THE OLYMPIC GAMES

The Statue of Zeus at Olympia was the most famous artistic work in all of ancient Greece and was one of the Seven Wonders of the Ancient World; it made a profound impression on all who saw it. Pausanias, a Greek traveler who wrote the earliest guidebook to ancient Greece in 150 A.D., described the statue in great detail; yet he also wrote that "records fall far short of the impression made by a sight of the image." To the Greeks the statue of Olympian Zeus was the incarnate god, and not to have seen it at least once in one's lifetime was considered a misfortune.

Ruling over the gods from his exalted throne atop Mount Olympus, Zeus saw everything, rewarded good conduct, punished evil, and governed all. He was the bringer of thunder and lightning, rain, and winds, and his weapon was the thunderbolt. He was the protector of cities, the home, strangers, and supplicants. Altars to Zeus graced the forecourts of houses throughout Greece, and pilgrims visited his many mountaintop shrines, but the god's best-known temple was the monumental Temple of Zeus, built in 460 B.C. in a sacred grove between two rivers at Olympia.

Within this temple the statue of the supreme god sat upon an intricately carved cedarwood throne that was decorated with mythical scenes of lesser gods and heroes rendered in gold, ebony, and precious stones. In his left hand Zeus carried a scepter made of a multicolored alloy of rare metals; crowned with an eagle's head, it symbolized his rule over the earth. His extended right hand supported a life-size statue of Nike, the goddess of victory, and the stool beneath his feet was upheld by two impressive gold lions. His hair, beard, and clothing were made of gold, and his head, hands, and feet were rendered in burnished ivory. To keep the ivory from cracking, the god had to be regularly anointed with olive oil, which was collected in a shallow pool beneath his feet. Over 40 feet in height, Zeus would have been too large to fit in the temple if he stood up—a curious fact to ancient commentators, who thought of the temple as Zeus's actual home.

Zeus presided over the Olympic games, a great Panhellenic festival that took place once every four years. Even in times of war, athletes from cities throughout Greece journeyed to Olympia to compete in the festival's contests of strength,

The Statue of Zeus at Olympia
One of the Wonders of the Ancient World
Olympia, Greece, 430 B.C.

(BASED ON RECONSTRUCTIONS OF THE STATUE BY J. SWADDLING AND MARTIN PRICE.)

AMAZEing ART: Wonders of the Ancient World, by Chris Berg ■ HarperCollins*Publishers*

endurance, and skill. Only Greek men were allowed in the games, and athletes had to swear a solemn oath before the altar of Zeus that they had trained for at least ten months and would compete fairly. Events included footraces, chariot and horse races, the discus and javelin throw, boxing, wrestling, and the broad jump. Combination events were popular, such as the *pancration*, a violent free-for-all that combined wrestling and boxing, and the *pentathlon*, which included running, wrestling, and javelin throwing. Runners were judged not only by their place at the finish line but also by their form, and thus the second- or third-place finisher often won the event. The athletes covered their bodies with oil, and competition was in the nude. Married women were excluded from watching—under penalty of being hurled from the heights of the nearby Typaeon rock.

Victors received only a simple laurel of wild olive leaves and the right to erect a statue at Olympia; by the time of Pausanias, over three thousand such statues crowded the site. But Olympic champions were hailed as heroes: Poets sang their praises, sculptors reproduced their images, and in their home cities, walls were torn down to make way for their triumphant return. Athletes from Athens even enjoyed free dinners in the state dining hall for the rest of their lives.

At its height in the fifth century B.C., the Olympic games drew crowds of over 40,000 from all across the Greek world: Athens, Sparta, Syracuse, Rhodes, and dozens of other cities. The statue of Zeus presided over the games until 393 A.D., when they were abolished by the Roman Emperor Theodosius I because of their pagan associations. The fate of the statue is unknown. Theodosius II ordered the destruction of the temple at Olympia in 426 A.D., and the statue might have perished then or been carried off to Constantinople, to be lost in the great fire that engulfed that city in 475 A.D. Subsequently neglected for 1,500 years, the Olympic games were revived in 1896 through the efforts of Baron Pierre de Coubertin of France.

"If anyone who is heavy-laden in mind, who has drained the cup of misfortune and sorrow in life, and who sweet sleep visits no more, were to stand before this statue, he would forget all the griefs and troubles of this mortal life."

—DION CHRYSOSTOM, GREEK RHETORICIAN AND PHILOSOPHER, FIRST CENTURY A.D.

"Aemilius visited the temple in Olympia, and when he saw the statue of Zeus he was awestruck, and said simply that Phidias seemed to him to have been the only artist who had made a likeness of Homer's Zeus; for he himself had come to Olympia with high expectations but the reality had far surpassed them."

—POLYBIOS, GREEK STATESMAN AND HISTORIAN, SECOND CENTURY B.C.

THE EXPANSION OF THE GREEK WORLD

"GREAT IS ARTEMIS OF THE EPHESIANS!"

"I have seen the walls and Hanging Gardens of ancient Babylon, the statue of Olympian Zeus, the Colossus of Rhodes, the mighty work of the high pyramids and the tomb of Mausolus. But when I saw the temple at Ephesus rising to the clouds, all these other wonders were put in the shade."

—PHILON OF BYZANTIUM, SCIENTIST AND ENGINEER, FIRST CENTURY B.C.

The road that linked the Greeks to the mysterious world of the Near East was an ancient trading route that connected Mesopotamia to the rocky shores of the Aegean Sea. It was one of the earliest long-distance roads ever constructed, and merchant caravans laden with exotic goods had plied its long course a thousand years before the Egyptians built the pyramids. The road began at Susa, the ancient capital of the kingdom of Elam at the foot of the Zagros mountains in Iran. Winding 1,500 miles across the fertile crescent, it passed through the exotic caravan centers at Nineveh and Harran, the deserts of Syria, and the pine forests on the slopes of the Taurus mountains in Anatolia. The end of the line was an idyllic river valley on the shore of the Aegean, home to the port city of Ephesus and a Greek temple that was one of the Wonders of the Ancient World.

As the focal point where many cultures met, Ephesus had a rich history. Croesus, the King of Lydia who was renowned for his great wealth, conquered the city sometime before 560 B.C. It was at Ephesus in 33 B.C. that Antony and Cleopatra, living in Persian splendor, marshaled their forces to battle Octavian—the future Emperor Augustus—in a final bid for the Roman Empire. The Ephesians believed their city to be the last home of the Virgin Mary, who lodged with St. John while he wrote his Gospel in the city. Ephesus's outdoor theater was the site of a famous protest against the missionary teachings of St. Paul, when a crowd of thousands of Ephesians chanted in unison, "Great is Artemis of the Ephesians! Great is Artemis of the Ephesians!" for two hours, forcing Paul and his disciples to leave the city by nightfall.

The Artemis that the Ephesians were celebrating was the goddess of wild animals and the hunt, vegetation, chastity, and childbirth. She had been worshipped in various forms throughout the Mediterranean since early times, but her most important shrine was at Ephesus: the Temple of Artemis, or Artemesion. This temple was celebrated throughout the ancient world not only for its great size (413 by 214 feet) but also for the magnificent marble sculptures that adorned its columns and pediments. Its intricately carved columns were said to have been 60 feet high, slender, and beautifully fluted; the stone lintel over its entranceway was so huge that one of the

AMAZEing ART: Wonders of the Ancient World, by Chris Berg ✠ HarperCollins*Publishers*

The Temple of Artemis in Ruins (a Fantasy)
One of the Wonders of the Ancient World
Anatolia, Third Century B.C.

"King Croesus, watching Persian soldiers sack [his capital city], is supposed to have asked the Persian King Cyrus, 'What is it that all those men of yours are so intent upon doing?' 'They are plundering your city and carrying off your treasures,' Cyrus replied. 'Not my city or my treasures,' Croesus corrected him. 'Nothing there any longer belongs to me. It is you they are robbing.'"

—Diodorus Siculus, Greek historian, first century B.C.

architects reputedly considered suicide when contemplating the task of setting it in place. Made almost entirely of gleaming white marble, the temple was first constructed in 560 B.C. under Croesus, who dedicated several golden cows that were kept within it. Also kept within the temple was a statue of Artemis, which was said to have fallen from the sky. This was partly true, for ancient commentators agreed that a holy stone that fell from the heavens—a meteorite—was housed in a small hollow inside the statue.

Croesus's early temple stood for over two hundred years, until one warm summer night in the year 356 B.C. when a man set a burning torch to it; as the flames spread, the building's cedar roof collapsed in an inferno of heat, and its magnificent stone columns cracked and toppled. The madman who committed this act had only one purpose: to immortalize his name as the man who had burned down the famed Artemesion. To prevent this the Ephesians, on pain of death, forbade the mentioning of his name. Despite this, his identity is known—but will not be repeated here.

With the aid of skilled artists and architects, the Ephesians rebuilt their temple. Antipater of Sidon, the second-century-B.C. writer who compiled an early list of the Seven Wonders, considered the rebuilt Artemesion to be the most glorious wonder of them all. It could not match the imposing bulk of the mysterious pyramids, nor the consummate artistry of the statue of Zeus at Olympia, but Antipater saw an elegance in the Temple of Artemis that was unmatched elsewhere. He wrote: "When I'd seen where Artemis's temple kisses the clouds, these lost their sheen. This side of heaven, I swear, the sun gains no sight so fair."

The rebuilt Artemesion was plundered and razed to the ground by invading Goths in 262 A.D., only months after a severe earthquake damaged Ephesus. The city never recovered its former splendor, and a few scattered stones and a slight depression in a swampy plain are all that now mark the spot where the Artemesion once stood.

THE MAUSOLEUM:
A TOMB TO RIVAL
THE EGYPTIAN PYRAMIDS

Located at the crossroads of the major ancient civilizations, Anatolia has been home to ever-shifting small kingdoms throughout its varied history. One of the rulers who stands out in the history of the region is Mausolus of Halicarnassus, a provincial governor, or *satrap*, of the Persian Empire from 377 to 353 B.C. His monumental tomb, the so-called Mausoleum, was one of the Seven Wonders of the Ancient World.

A shrewd politician, Mausolus gambled on the shifting alliances among the Persian, Egyptian, and Greek empires of his time. Not long after assuming power he took part in a revolt of the Persian governors in Anatolia against Artaxerxes II, the Persian king. The revolt was unsuccessful, but Mausolus had abandoned his allies just in time to keep from going down in defeat with them. Just one year later he changed sides and joined with Artaxerxes in a punitive war against the Egyptians, who had backed the revolt. He also supported the islands of Rhodes, Cos, and Chios in a successful war against Athens, bringing their cities into his sphere of influence.

Mausolus was an unscrupulous ruler. He tricked the citizens of Mylasa into donating large sums for the construction of a defensive wall to protect their city, but after the money was collected, he stated that the gods would not allow the wall to be built. Instead, he took his newly acquired wealth and founded a new capital at Halicarnassus. Mausolus was apparently not without a sense of humor, however, for he once convinced the Lycians that the Persian king had issued orders that all their hair must be donated to make wigs for Persian ladies. But if the Lycians were willing to pay, Mausolus said, he could use his personal influence to save their hair by giving the king some of their gold instead. The Lycians promptly paid up, and Mausolus pocketed the gold.

When Mausolus died in 353 B.C. after consolidating a small empire, his wife Artemisia completed the construction of a tomb for him that would vie with the Egyptian pyramids in its magnificence and splendor. Artemisia's devotion to her hus-

> "I have lying over me in Halicarnassus a gigantic monument such as no other dead person has, adorned in the finest way with statues of horses and men realistically carved from the finest marble."
>
> —KING MAUSOLUS, IN LUCIAN'S "DIALOGUES OF THE DEAD"

The Mausoleum at Halicarnassus
One of the Wonders of the Ancient World
Anatolia, 350 B.C.

(BASED ON A RECONSTRUCTION OF THE MONUMENT BY BERNEIR.)

band's memory was undoubtedly strengthened because he was also her brother—a marriage custom not unheard of in Egypt, but alien to the Greeks. She summoned to Halicarnassus some of the most talented sculptors and architects of the age and set them to work building a suitable monument to the memory of her husband and brother. Artemisia herself died before these famous artists could complete their work, but Pliny recorded that they continued to work on the monument to immortalize their own "glory and artistic skill."

The monument they built to Mausolus was set upon a platform of six steps. The first stage of the building was a stone wall decorated with two rows of painted marble sculptures in relief set one atop the other. Above this, 36 Ionic columns, placed in an 11-by-9-column rectangle, supported a pyramidal roof. There were statues between all the columns and the roof was decorated with lions, which were a symbol of kingship and were also intended to scare off tomb robbers. The crowning feature was a 24-step pyramid surmounted by a larger-than-life-size sculpture of Mausolus and Artemisia riding a chariot drawn by four marble horses. The tomb, over 140 feet in height, was truly a monumental sight.

The Mausoleum was thrown down by an earthquake sometime between the twelfth and fourteenth centuries A.D. In the fifteenth century its remains were systematically plundered by the Knights of St. John (later to become famous as the Knights of Malta), who were building a fortress in the harbor at Halicarnassus. For a hundred years these zealous crusaders would be the scourge of Muslim Turks from their naval base on nearby Rhodes. When modern scholars finally found the foundations of the Mausoleum, excavators discovered several column drums, a few fragments of statues and sculptural reliefs, and some decorative lions. These scant remains were all that had escaped the grasp of the redoubtable Knights of St. John.

"Taking candles, they went down into the chamber and found marble columns carved in relief. The space between the columns was lined with mouldings and sculptures, and histories and battle scenes were also represented in relief. Having admired this at first, and entertained their fancy with the singularity of the work, finally they pulled it down, broke it apart and smashed it, in order to use it [for the lime kilns]."

—THE KNIGHTS OF ST. JOHN DISCOVERING MAUSSOLLOS'S BURIAL CHAMBER, AS DESCRIBED BY CLAUDE GUICHARD, 1581

THE FALLEN GIANT
OF RHODES

In 305 B.C. Antigonus the One-Eyed, a powerful ruler of Macedonia and one of Alexander the Great's most successful generals, called upon the island of Rhodes to join him in a war against his rival, King Ptolemy I of Egypt. The Rhodians, however, could ill afford to go to war with Egypt, their largest trading partner, and so they refused Antigonus's offer. To express his displeasure with this descision, Antigonus sent his son Demetrius Poliorcetes ("the Besieger") to attack Rhodes with an army of 40,000 soldiers. Demetrius was skilled in directing catapults and battering rams to crush city walls, and upon landing on the island he immediately began his efforts to break down its fortifications and defenses. Demetrius's tortoise-like armored battering rams were 180 feet long and manned by one thousand men, and his giant catapults threw 180-pound stone balls a quarter of a mile. Probably his most fearsome device was one of his enormous wheeled fortified towers, which he called Helepolis (the "Taker of Cities"). This tower was 50 feet square at its base, more than 100 feet tall, and armed with its own banks of catapults and sling throwers. The outlook for the island was grim.

Surprisingly, the people of Rhodes put up a daring resistance, and with some help from King Ptolemy their cities withstood the assault. When several of Demetrius's siege towers were destroyed—mired down in mud created by the Rhodians, who flooded the enemy encampment—Antigonus realized that his son's forces could no longer prevail, and ordered Demetrius to make terms and abandon the island. Demetrius reluctantly moved on to other conquests, but he left behind many of his expensive siege engines as a gift, reputedly because he was impressed with the spirit of the Rhodians' resistance (even their slaves had manned the city walls).

The Rhodians immediately set about erecting a suitable monument to their victory. They had been praying to their patron god Helios for deliverance throughout the ordeal, so they dismantled the abandoned siege engines, sold the wood and metal as scrap, and used the resulting money to pay for an enormous statue—the Colossus of Helios at Rhodes. The Colossus took twelve years to complete, and was said to have

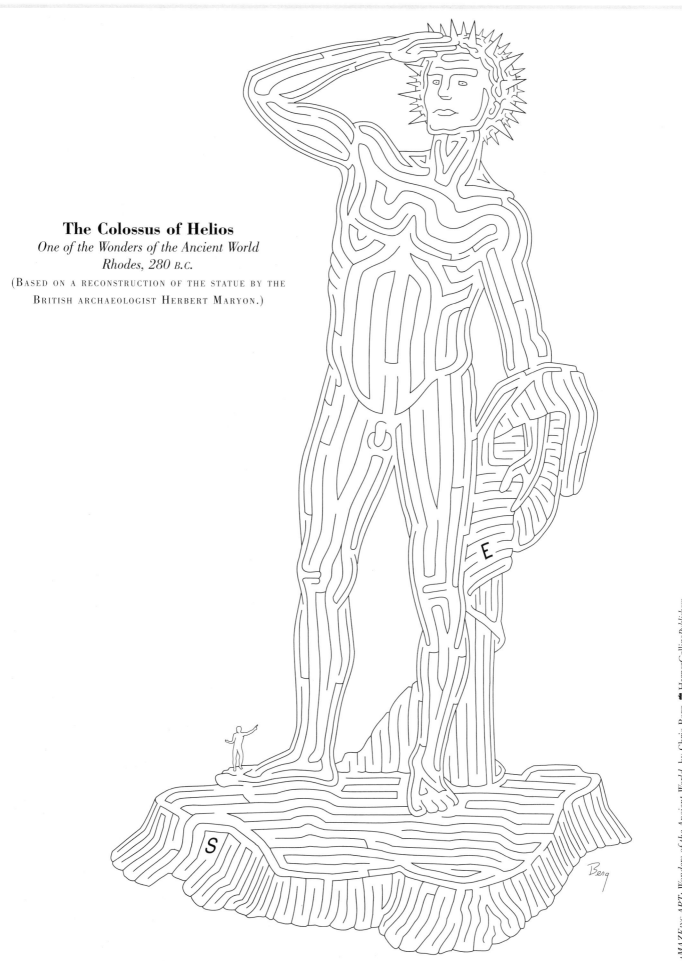

The Colossus of Helios
One of the Wonders of the Ancient World
Rhodes, 280 B.C.
(Based on a reconstruction of the statue by the
British archaeologist Herbert Maryon.)

aMAZEing ART: Wonders of the Ancient World, by Chris Berg ⬛ HarperCollinsPublishers

"At Rhodes was set up a Colossus of seventy cubits high, representing the Sun. The artist expended as much bronze on it as seemed likely to create a dearth in the mines, for the casting of the statue was an operation in which the bronze industry of the whole world was concerned."

—PHILO OF BYZANTIUM, SCIENTIST AND ENGINEER, FIRST CENTURY B.C.

caused a shortage of bronze throughout the ancient world during its construction. It stood about 110 feet from head to toe—only slightly smaller than the Statue of Liberty—and consisted of a bronze outer skin supported by an internal frame of stone columns and iron bars. The burning rays of the sun-god Helios were cast in bronze emanating from its head. Placed upon a 50-foot marble pedestal, the statue's great size ensured that it was visible to ships approaching Rhodes from many miles away. It must have seemed an indestructible monument to the growing power and prestige of Rhodes.

As fate would have it, however, an untimely end was destined for the Colossus. In 224 B.C., only 65 years after its completion, the statue was toppled by a strong earthquake, crushing many houses as it fell. King Ptolemy III immediately offered to pay for it to be rebuilt, but the Rhodians had been warned by an oracle to let it lie and so declined his generous offer. The statue lay where it fell for over 875 years until Arab invaders pillaged its remains and sent the scrap metal to Syria, where it was carried off on the backs of 900 camels to be melted down—probably into bronze lamps. Nothing of the Colossus remains today, and the site upon which it once stood has not been positively identified.

The fallen ruins of the Colossus inspired as much awe as had the standing monument. A Greek named Strabo, who wrote one of the first books on geography, described its ruins: "The finest of all the votive gifts and statues in the city of Rhodes is the Colossus of Helios. Now it lies on the ground, overthrown by an earthquake, severed at the knees." In Roman times the fallen Colossus was a popular tourist attraction; Pliny the Elder visited it and wrote: "Even lying on the ground it is a marvel. Few people can make their arms meet round its thumbs, and its fingers are larger than most statues." In the Middle Ages—several centuries after the remains of the statue had been scrapped—all sorts of exaggerated tales were circulated about the Colossus. Among other things it was said to have been 900 feet tall and to bestride the harbor of Rhodes so that ships could pass beneath its legs.

This labyrinth puzzle is based on work by archaeologist Herbert Maryon, who reconstructed the Colossus from the few archaeological clues that remain. More recent reconstructions suggest that the Colossus's outstretched arm was raised high above its head, much like the Statue of Liberty—which was, in fact, inspired by it.

"Why, man, he doth bestride the narrow world

Like a Colossus; and we petty men

Walk under his huge legs, and peep about . . . "

—WILLIAM SHAKESPEARE,
Julius Caesar

THE PHAROS
OF ALEXANDRIA:
CELEBRATED LIGHTHOUSE
OF ANTIQUITY

The Pharos of Alexandria, built during the third century B.C. on a small island in the harbor of Alexandria in Egypt, was the most famous lighthouse in the ancient world. A huge stone tower protected from the sea by a walled platform, it consisted of three stages: the lowest was square with slightly tapered sides, the middle octagonal, and the topmost cylindrical. It was crowned with a statue, probably of Zeus or Poseidon, and housed an open fire magnified by a burnished bronze reflector that guided ships safely into the harbor of Alexandria. The fire was kept burning night and day, and fuel was delivered via a shaft that rose to the topmost stage. At 350 feet in height the Pharos was nearly as tall as the pyramids, and was the first true high-rise building in the history of architecture.

The Pharos took fifteen years to construct, and when it was completed around 283 B.C. the King of Egypt, Ptolemy II, gave the customary order that his name alone was to appear on the foundation stone. But the crafty engineer who had designed the Pharos, Sostratos of Cnidus, instead inscribed on the stone these words: "SOSTRATOS SON OF DEXIPHANES OF CNIDUS ON BEHALF OF ALL MARINERS TO THE SAVIOR GODS." This he covered over with plaster, upon which the king's lofty inscription was carved. Long after both Sostratos and the king were dead, the plaster inscription crumbled away, revealing to all visitors the true identity of the monument's builder.

Sostratos's cleverness exemplifies a change that was occurring in the Hellenistic (or Greek-speaking) world in the third century B.C., when the pronouncements of kings and oracles were being eclipsed by the work of engineers and scientists. Alexander the Great had recently wrested control of much of the known world from the Persians, and Egypt was ruled by the Ptolemies, a dynasty of Greek kings. With just 4,000 Greek soldiers the earliest Ptolemies governed all of Egypt

> "The courses of the stones are united by molten lead, and the joints are so adherent that the whole is indissoluble, though the surge of the sea from the north incessantly beats against the structure."
>
> —IDRISI, SPANISH ARCHITECT, TWELFTH CENTURY A.D., DESCRIBING THE PHAROS

The Pharos of Alexandria
One of the Wonders of the Ancient World
Alexandria, Egypt, 283 B.C.
(Based on a reconstruction of the Pharos by the
German archaeologist Hermann Thiersch.)

AMAZEng ART: Wonders of the Ancient World, by Chris Berg ⊞ HarperCollins Publishers

from their new capital at Alexandria. Chosen by Alexander himself for its natural advantages as a seaport, the new city quickly grew into the largest and most vibrant commercial center in the ancient Mediterranean. Its cosmopolitan mix of half a million Greeks, Egyptians, and Jews soon developed a new morality—one based as much on the primacy of human knowledge as on the worship of the gods.

Attracted by the Museum (the "Shrine of the Muses"), a district of the city dedicated to learning, the best minds of the age came to study at Alexandria: men such as Euclid, who first developed the method of mathematical proof by axioms; Archimedes, who is said to have invented the screw while in Egypt; and Erastothenes, who accurately calculated the circumference of the earth by comparing the length of shadows in different cities on the same day. When these men were in Alexandria, they studied in the Great Library, the largest library in the ancient world, with 700,000 books written on papyrus scrolls in its collection. By royal decree, all travelers to Egypt had to surrender their books to the Library, which then copied them, kept the originals, and returned the copies to the travelers.

The Pharos's bright beacon captured the spirit of the Hellenistic age in Alexandria, but it would not endure. The Great Library was burned to the ground in a series of fires beginning in Roman times, and Alexandria was abandoned to the advancing Arabs without a fight in the seventh century A.D. Legend recorded that the Pharos was nearly destroyed by the Arabs after the Byzantine Emperor, wishing to harm their trade, sent word that treasure was hidden within it. The Arab ruler set his men to demolishing the lighthouse, and they did not realize the trick that had been played upon them until it was half destroyed. Whatever the truth behind this story, the Pharos was finally toppled by an earthquake in the fourteenth century, and its scattered remains were incorporated into a fortress not long thereafter. By the time of Napoleon's expedition to Egypt in 1798, the great city of Alexandria itself was nothing more than a sleepy fishing village.

"By founding Alexandria, Alexander achieved more fame than with all his brilliant victories. This is the city that had to become the heart of the world."

—NAPOLEON BONAPARTE, 1798

"[Alexander] decided to found a great city in Egypt, and gave orders to the men left behind with this mission to build the city between the marsh and the sea. He laid out the site and traced the streets skillfully and ordered that the city should be called after him Alexandria. It was conveniently situated near the harbour of Pharos, and by selecting the right angle of the streets, Alexander made the city breathe with the etesian winds so that, as these blow across a great expanse of sea, they cool the air of the town . . ."

—DIODORUS SICULUS,
GREEK HISTORIAN,
FIRST CENTURY B.C.

The Romans:
Splendor
and Excess

THE FORUM:
HEART OF ROME

At its height in the second century A.D., Rome was so famed that people often simply referred to it as "Urbs"—the City. It was home to nearly a million people and boasted 1,500 public fountains, 28 libraries, a dozen enormous bath complexes, hundreds of public squares, and a collection of palaces and temples unrivaled in the ancient world. At the center of this vast sprawl, in a small valley ringed by the Seven Hills, sat the Roman Forum. An open meeting area surrounded by public buildings and colonnades, the Forum was the political, commercial, and cultural center of the city—the heart of Rome.

Enormous crowds gathered in the Forum at all hours. Senators on their way to the assembly, lawyers meeting with their clients, street vendors selling goods from every corner of the empire, and ordinary citizens all mingled with each other. In the words of the comic dramatist Plautus, you could meet "whatever fellow you wanted to meet, honorable or the reverse" in the Forum, from respectable and well-to-do couples out for a walk to men and women for hire or purchase. Many of the city's most impressive temples and monuments were in the Forum, such as the Temple of Saturn, which served as the state treasury; the Temple of Vesta, home to the Vestal Virgins and the sacred, undying flame they guarded; and the Milliarium Aureum, the golden milestone inscribed with the distances to all the major cities in the empire. The senate and law courts met nearby, and the Forum was even used for early gladiatorial combats and public and private banquets.

The Forum was popular in part because it was a place where citizens could go to share in the majesty that was Rome, for their city was not so attractive when viewed from the large apartment houses, or *insulae*, in which the average Roman lived. These were dark, overcrowded, dismal buildings up to seven stories in height and often infested with rats, and they frequently collapsed or burned up in fires due to shoddy construction practices. The great orator Cicero complained of them: "Two of my shops have fallen down and the rest are cracking; not only have the tenants fled but even the mice have migrated."

"The Arrius Pollio Apartment Complex owned by Gnaeus Allius Nigidius Maius FOR RENT from July 1st. Streetfront shops with counter space, Luxurious second-story apartments, And a townhouse. Prospective renters, please make arrangements with Primus, slave of Gnaeus Allius Nigidius Maius."

—ROMAN RENTAL NOTICE FROM POMPEII, FIRST CENTURY A.D.

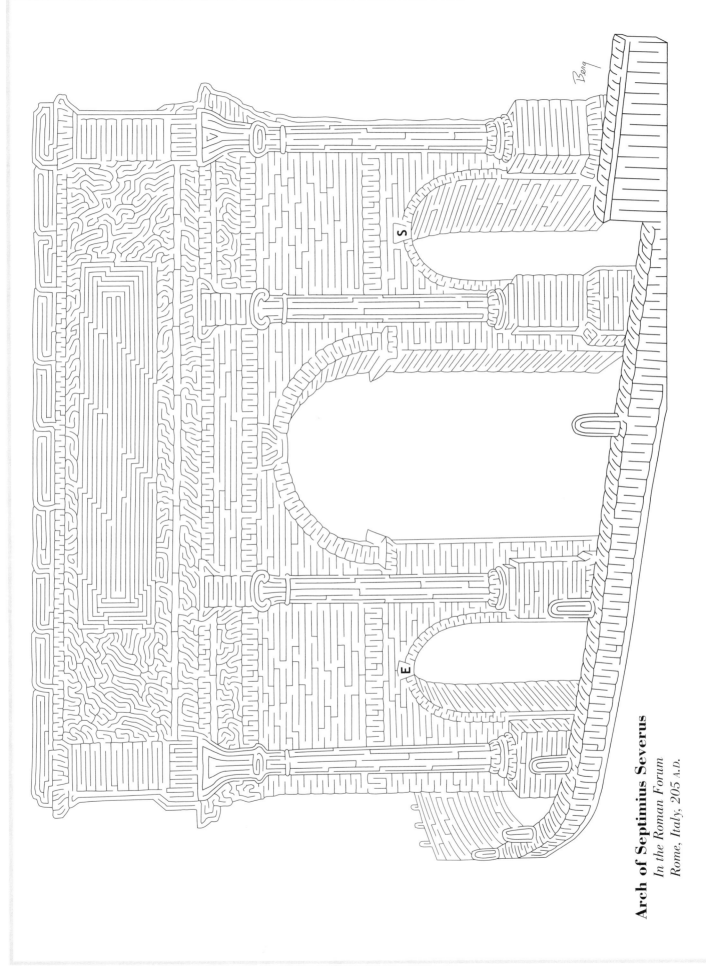

Arch of Septimius Severus
In the Roman Forum
Rome, Italy, 205 A.D.

*A*MAZE*ING ART: Wonders of the Ancient World,* by Chris Berg ■ HarperCollins*Publishers*

All kinds of things, from the momentous to the bizarre, occurred in the Forum. The deranged Emperor Caligula—who once ordered his armies in Gaul to collect seashells, which he called the "spoils of the conquered ocean"—used to scatter large sums of money to crowds of people from the balconies of the law courts. Late at night one might encounter a group of young men, with an emperor such as Nero among them, out for an evening of assaulting women and looting stores. Caesar threw an enormous banquet for the entire city in the Forum to celebrate his military victories; he would later be assassinated there by his friend Brutus and other conspirators. The most spectacular events that occurred in the Forum, however, were undoubtedly the Triumphal processions.

The Triumphal processions were the highest honor bestowed in ancient Rome. In the early days they were given to victorious generals whose armies had slain at least 5,000 of the enemy in an important battle; later only emperors would be granted the honor. Along streets decorated with flowers and lined with crowds chanting "Io triumphe!" the Roman Senate came first in a grand procession, followed by musicians and sacrificial animals, the spoils of war, and the captured prisoners. These often included great kings and princes of vanquished countries, and placards giving the names of conquered territories were borne before each group of captives. Wearing a royal purple and gold toga, the triumphant general came next upon a chariot. A slave held a golden crown of victory over the general's head, while repeatedly whispering, amid the adulation of the crowds, that the general was still a mortal man and not a god. The last members of the procession were the soldiers, who marched along singing bawdy songs about their commander.

In the later Roman Empire, the so-called triumphal arches, such as the Arch of Septimius Severus in the Forum, were erected to permanently immortalize the victories of the emperors. Thirty-six of them used to dot the city, but only three remain standing today. Severus's arch was built in 203 A.D. after he returned from a campaign in the East, but the emperor allegedly was so crippled by gout that he could not stand up on a chariot, and so had to forgo his triumph.

"Enrich the soldiers, despise all the others."

—EMPEROR SEVERUS'S ADVICE TO HIS SONS AS HE LAY DYING, 211 A.D.

"On the day of Caesar's Gallic triumph, the axle of the triumphal car broke . . . and he nearly fell out. Later, he went up to the capitol between two rows of elephants, of which there were 40 in all. In the Pontic triumph, on one of the floats, instead of the usual tableau showing scenes from the campaign, there was an inscription of three words only: VENI, VIDI, VICI ('I came, I saw, I conquered'), thus showing the speed of the whole operation."

—SUETONIUS, ROMAN BIOGRAPHER, FIRST CENTURY A.D.

THE ROMAN AQUEDUCTS

In 152 A.D. a Roman engineer named Nonius Datus traveled to Algeria to inspect an aqueduct under construction in the city of Saldae. Part of the aqueduct's course went through a large mountain, and following Datus's earlier instructions workmen had been tunneling into this mountain from both ends, intending to meet in the middle. Upon his arrival, however, Datus found to his dismay that each section of the tunnel had been excavated beyond the half-way point, and the two ends had not met. The workmen, who had been hewing through solid rock for four years, were angry and despondent. The contractor blamed Datus, who had originally surveyed the tunnel and then left to work on other projects, while Datus accused the contractor of having made "blunder upon blunder [so that] each section of the tunnel diverged from the straight line."

We will probably never know who was at fault in this curiously modern-sounding story of a construction fiasco. Lacking suitable pressurized piping, Roman aqueducts had to rely on gravity for a constant flow of water, and engineers such as Nonius Datus bridged ravines and tunneled through mountains to maintain the often imperceptible downgrade—typically a few feet per mile—that was required in order for them to function properly. But bridges and tunnels were costly and sometimes risky ventures, and the Romans preferred to go around obstacles whenever they could. Though they are the most conspicuous parts of the Roman aqueducts, elegant arched bridges such as the Pont du Gard formed only a small part of the whole system. Most of the length of an aqueduct consisted of a simple stone conduit dug in the ground, lined with waterproof cement or lead to prevent leakage.

The first Roman aqueduct was built in 312 B.C. and brought water to the city of Rome from the nearby Anio river. As the city's population grew over the next few centuries, eight others were added, and by the first century A.D. Rome received hundreds of millions of gallons of water per day from its nine aqueducts—more water per person than many modern cities can provide. The later aqueducts are spectacular reworkings of nature (the largest was 56 miles in length) whose sheer scale ensures their place among the marvels of engineering in the ancient world.

The Romans considered the water from each of their aqueducts to be best for certain uses—one was unfit for anything except watering plants—and they rarely

"Will anybody compare the Pyramids, or those useless though renowned works of the Greeks, with these aqueducts?"

—FRONTINUS, ROMAN WATER COMMISSIONER, FIRST CENTURY A.D.

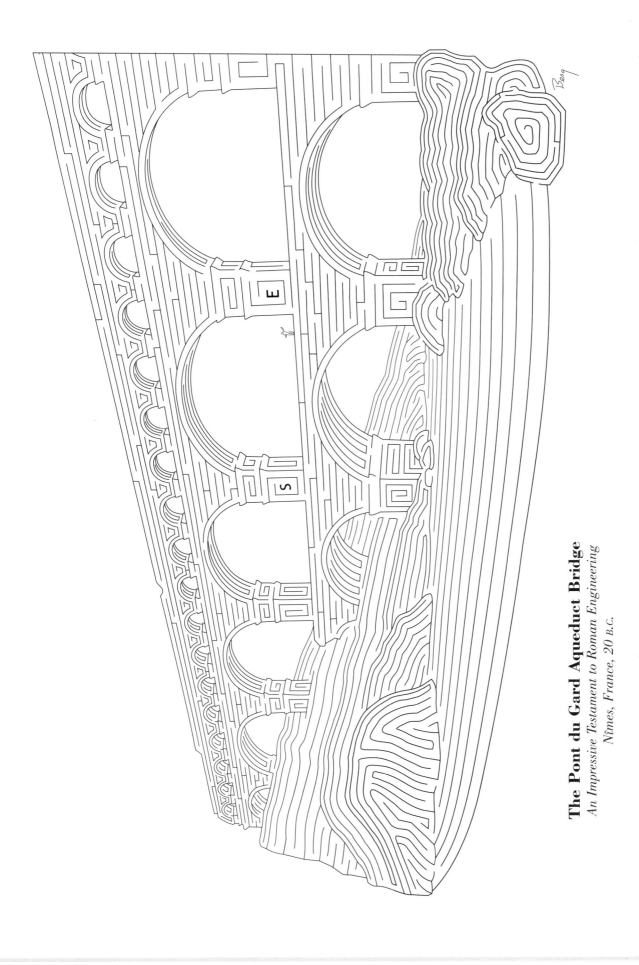

The Pont du Gard Aqueduct Bridge

An Impressive Testament to Roman Engineering

Nîmes, France, 20 B.C.

"If we consider the distances traversed by the water before it arrives, the raising of the arches, the tunneling of mountains and the building of level routes across deep valleys, we shall readily admit that there has never been anything more remarkable in the whole world."

—PLINY THE ELDER, ROMAN AUTHOR AND STATESMAN, FIRST CENTURY A.D.

mixed them. Each aqueduct had its own distribution system consisting of settling tanks and lead pipes that connected it to public baths and fountains, industrial establishments, or a select few private homes and apartment houses. The water was unpressurized, so Roman apartment buildings had running water on the ground floor only. Most citizens had to get their water themselves at the public fountains, or buy it from the criminal gangs that monopolized the corrupt business of door-to-door water delivery in the city. Some Romans chose to secretly bore holes to connect their homes and shops to the distribution pipes; when Frontinus became water commissioner in the first century A.D., he was appalled at the scale of such fraud and theft.

Most of the water from the aqueducts went to the public baths, or *thermae* as the Romans called them. Originally places to get clean, the Roman baths gradually evolved into enormous recreational complexes containing hot and cold baths, swimming pools, saunas, gymnastic and exercise rooms, gardens, lecture halls, and libraries. Sumptuously decorated with frescoes, mosaics, and sculptures, the baths were popular places to socialize and conduct business, and the Romans visited them on a daily basis. By the middle of the second century A.D. there were several hundred public baths in Rome, including those of the Emperor Caracalla, which covered an area of 27 acres, held 21 million gallons of water, and entertained 2,000 bathers at a time. Such vast complexes were noisy places; the philosopher Seneca complained of how horrible it was to have an apartment next to one, constantly hearing the grunts of the gymnasts as they swung their weights, the splashing of the swimmers, and the cries of the sausage vendors. Yet it was the increasing popularity of the baths that drove the construction of magnificent aqueducts throughout the Empire. Such was the glory of Rome.

THE BARBARIC
SPECTACLE OF THE ARENA

Sometime around 385 A.D. a man named Alypius—a friend of St. Augustine's—came to Rome to study law, and there became obsessed with a perverse enthusiasm for gladiatorial combat. A quiet and sensitive man, he shunned the decadence of Roman society and at first refused to enter the Colosseum. But one day, after a chance encounter with a group of friends who swept aside his protestations, he found himself at the games.

Once seated, Alypius immediately covered his eyes, refusing to look upon the combat. But he could not also cover his ears, and when an incident in the fighting provoked a great roar from the crowd, Alypius was startled and looked out upon the Arena. As St. Augustine relates, Alypius then "riveted his gaze on the scene and took in all its frightfulness, unaware of what he was doing. The thrill of seeing blood shed was an intoxication. No longer was he the man who had been dragged to the Arena. He watched, he cheered, he sweated with excitement; when he left, his mind was so contaminated that he had no peace till he could go again."

The Romans called it the Flavian Amphitheater. Its construction, begun under Emperor Vespasian, was completed by his successor Titus in 80 A.D. Hundreds of arches decorated with statues of Roman gods supported its four stories, and it was covered with a huge circular awning to keep out the elements. Capable of seating up to 70,000 spectators, it dominated the skyline of Rome. Beneath the sands of its Arena lay a labyrinth of rooms, passageways, and mechanical elevators. Here, gladiators and animals alike awaited their turn in the combat.

There were many types of gladiators, including the Samnites, who fought with a round shield and a short sword; the *retiarius*, who wielded a trident and a net, and the *dimachaeri*, who carried two short swords. Often two different types would be set against each other in single combat, and the Romans bet great sums of money on the outcomes of such duels. Entertaining the crowd was all-important and gladiators were taught how to fight in the most dramatic fashion, for when a gladiator was at the mercy of his opponent he lifted up his forefinger to implore the crowd, who decided his fate. If he had entertained them they would spare his life; a thumbs-up sign meant

"None of Emperor Titus's predecessors ever displayed such generosity. At the time of the dedication of the Flavian Amphitheatre . . . he provided a most lavish display of gladiators. He also displayed sea battles on the artificial lake . . . after the water had been let out, the basin was used for yet other gladiatorial contests and for a wild beast hunt, in which 5,000 animals of different kinds were dispatched in a single day. Titus was naturally kind-hearted . . ."

—SUETONIUS, ROMAN BIOGRAPHER, FIRST CENTURY A.D.

99

Ruins of the Colosseum

Considered a Wonder of the World by the Romans
Rome, Italy, 80 A.D.

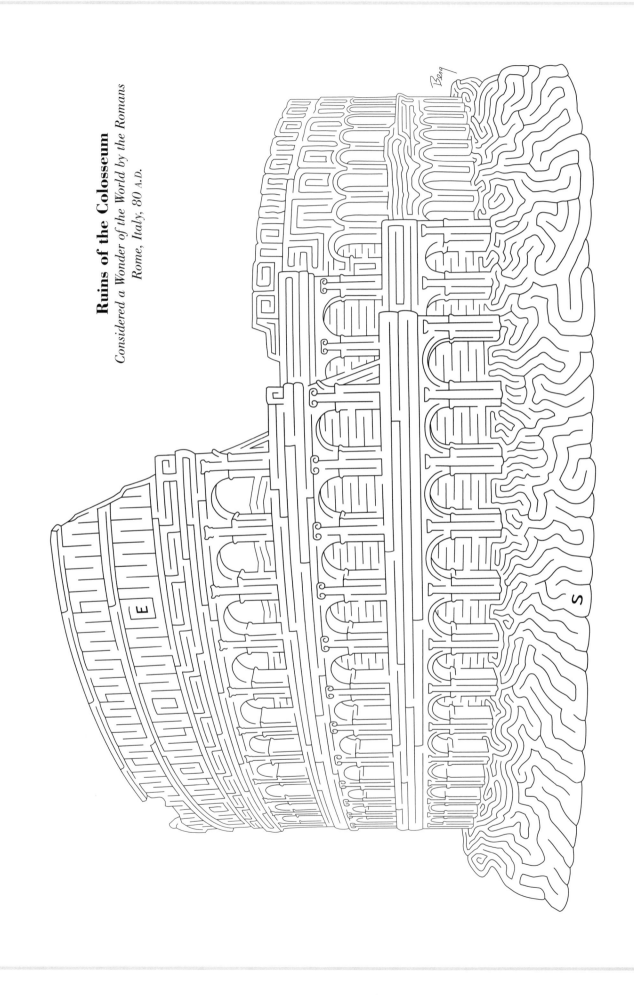

AMAZEing ART: *Wonders of the Ancient World,* by Chris Berg ■ HarperCollins*Publishers*

death. Combats between gladiators and animals were the most popular with the crowds, and the Romans searched the known world for lions, bears, crocodiles, hippopotamuses, and other rarer animals for these events, driving some species to extinction.

Most gladiators were criminals, prisoners, or slaves, but some men volunteered for the games hoping for fame and reward; successful gladiators could become the personal bodyguards of emperors and enjoyed the attentions of society women. The half-mad emperor Commodus, imagining himself to be Hercules, even appeared in the games. He slew unarmed opponents and the crowds wildly applauded his exploits; but he began to believe they mocked him, and one day—if we can believe the words of an unknown writer—he supposedly ordered his soldiers to slaughter everyone in the Colosseum.

Admission to the games was always free—the emperor's gift to the people. For three hundred years, successive emperors would strive to present ever more lavish games, which became the most popular events in Rome. In Trajan's celebrations 9,000 gladiators and 11,000 animals were killed in 117 days. Claudius devised the most violent events, in which hundreds of gladiators would try to dispatch each other in the shortest possible time. The Arena was flooded for mock naval battles, and innocent Christians really were thrown to wild animals to be torn to pieces. While all this was occurring, vendors sold snacks made from chickpea flour, as well as hot drinks, souvenirs, cushions, and blankets.

After the games were banned by Christian emperors, and the Roman Empire collapsed in the West, the Colosseum deteriorated. Pope Sixtus V's plans to convert its aging ruins into a wool factory to provide employment for Rome's less fortunate women came to naught. But it suffered damage from lightning, earthquakes, and especially vandalism. Until protected by Pope Pius VIII in the 1830s, the Colosseum had been used for centuries as a convenient quarry; all its marble seats and decorative materials have disappeared. Today it is an empty skeleton, and only stray cats duel in its ruins.

"Crescens, the net fighter, holds the hearts of all the girls. Celadus, the Thracian, makes all the girls sigh."

—GRAFFITI FROM POMPEII, FIRST CENTURY A.D.

THE PANTHEON:
EYE OF THE GODS

The Romans' mastery of building techniques reached its summit in the Pantheon. One of the great buildings in Western architecture, the Pantheon is remarkable both as a feat of engineering and for its manipulation of interior space—and for a time, it was also home to the largest pearl in the ancient world.

Originally built in 27 B.C. by the statesman Marcus Agrippa, the powerful deputy of Rome's first emperor, the Pantheon was completely redesigned and rebuilt in 118 A.D. under Emperor Hadrian. Hadrian was possessed with insatiable curiosity; one of his contemporaries called him an "explorer of everything interesting." He spent much of his long reign on four grand tours of the Empire, during which he learned about the cultures he ruled, sampled different cuisines, and met with everyone who interested him. While in Athens he was overcome by its architecture and art. He was a painter, a poet, a mathematician, but above all an architect and builder.

The Pantheon that Hadrian created is a circular temple made of concrete faced with brick, with a Greek-style facade and a magnificent dome rising from its walls. The most striking feature of the building is the 27-foot circular hole (the *oculus*, or eye) atop the dome. By day a great shaft of sunlight streams through it, illuminating the richly colored marble lining the dome's interior. To the Romans, this *oculus* symbolized the eye of the gods looking down upon their city. The temple was dedicated to all the Roman gods; all seven niches in the dome's interior contained their statues, notably those of Venus and Mars.

The Pantheon is one of the finest examples of the Romans' use of concrete. The Romans were the first to exploit this building material, and without its use the great imperial buildings of the Roman Empire would not have been possible. In the Pantheon's dome, the mix of concrete varied from heavy aggregate in the thick base to lightweight pumice at the top. Made of over 5,000 tons of concrete, the dome is 142 feet in diameter and 71 feet high, and was unsurpassed in size until the nineteenth century.

In 609 A.D. the Pantheon was converted to a church, and Italy's first two kings and many artists, including Raphael, are buried in it. In Roman times the largest

The Interior of the Pantheon
"An angelic, not a human, design."
Rome, Italy, 118 A.D.
(This view of the interior of the Pantheon was inspired by a drawing done
by the Italian artist Piranesi [1720–1778].)

aMAZEing ART: Wonders of the Ancient World, by Chris Berg ● HarperCollinsPublishers

pearl in the ancient world, which had belonged to Cleopatra, the last Queen of Egypt, was also kept in the Pantheon. How this pearl got there—and the fate of its twin, which was just as large—is a tale in itself.

The two largest pearls in the whole of history, according to Pliny, had come to Cleopatra from kings of the East. Cleopatra took them with her in 37 B.C. when she went to live with Mark Antony, who was vying with Octavian for control of the Empire. Mark Antony was glutting himself daily at ostentatious banquets, yet Cleopatra still reproached him with lofty pride for the meagerness of his feasts. Antony wondered what additional magnificence was possible, and to this Cleopatra replied that she could spend ten million sesterces on a banquet for them both. This was a fabulous sum; the Roman state treasury under Caesar contained thirty million sesterces. Antony declared it impossible, and bets were made.

The next day, Cleopatra served an unexceptional banquet. Antony laughed, thinking that he had won his bet, but servants then brought out a single bowl of vinegar. Antony could not contain his curiosity as Cleopatra, who had the remarkable pearls in her ears, took one off and dropped it in the bowl. The pearl slowly dissolved and Cleopatra drank it down. Before she could similarly dissolve the second pearl, Lucius Plancus—the umpire of the wager—placed his hand on her wrist and declared that "Antony had lost the battle."

When Cleopatra was captured after Antony had lost both the naval battle at Actium and the Roman Empire, the surviving pearl was cut in half and eventually placed on the ears of the statue of Venus in the Pantheon. And that is the story of how the largest pearl in the world ended up in the Pantheon at Rome.

"It is, as it were, the visible image of the universe."

—PERCY BYSSHE SHELLEY, ENGLISH ROMANTIC POET, 1820

"An angelic, not a human, design."

—MICHELANGELO, FIFTEENTH CENTURY A.D.

LORD CHOCOLATE BEAN AND THE MAYAN PYRAMIDS

"As they contained nothing in which there were not to be seen superstition and lies of the devil, we burned them all, which [the natives] regretted to an amazing degree."

—SPANISH BISHOP DIEGO DE LANDA, ON HIS SYSTEMATIC BURNING OF THOUSANDS OF MAYAN BOOKS IN THE SIXTEENTH CENTURY A.D.

In the winter of 1944 a photographer named Giles Healey set out for a remote area of the Chiapas jungle in southern Mexico. Healey was making a documentary film about indigenous Indians and sought a tribe known as the Lacandon, who had retreated into the wilderness following the Spanish conquest in the sixteenth century. All but forgotten by the outside world, they were the last untouched remnants of the Maya.

Healey found the Lacandon villages, and while making his film noticed a curious thing: Lacandon men often made secret pilgrimages deep into the jungle. When he finally persuaded them to take him along on these trips, Healey was led to a series of hidden ruins, where crumbling pyramidal temples, gnawed by the grasping fingers of monstrous vines, rose phantomlike out of the earth. The Lacandon were no longer able to read the elaborate glyphs that decorated these temples, yet they maintained the ancient shrines with great reverence, making regular offerings to the Mayan gods amid the sprawling wreckage of their forefathers.

Had they understood them, the Lacandon would surely have been amazed by the tales revealed in their ancestors' glyphs. Mayan civilization flourished between 400 B.C. and 900 A.D., and at its height consisted of about 40 major cities, each with its palaces, pyramidal temples, stadiumlike ball courts, aqueducts, and raised roads. Linked together by a complex network of commercial ties, the Mayan cities traded everything from beeswax and vegetable dyes to tobacco and rubber. The Maya practiced advanced techniques of terraced irrigation, developed an intricate and beautiful tradition of relief carving, and wrote books on paper manufactured from tree bark. Their mathematical system, one of the most advanced in the ancient world, was based on the number 20 (they counted on both fingers and toes) and included the use of zero. Mayan priests made meticulous observations of the sun, moon, and Venus over a 400-year period, and were able to predict solar eclipses. They also developed a sophisticated calendar that was more precise than the standard Gregorian calendar the world uses today. The many achievements of the Maya are all the more impressive considering that they had no metal tools, no draft animals, and no wheeled vehicles.

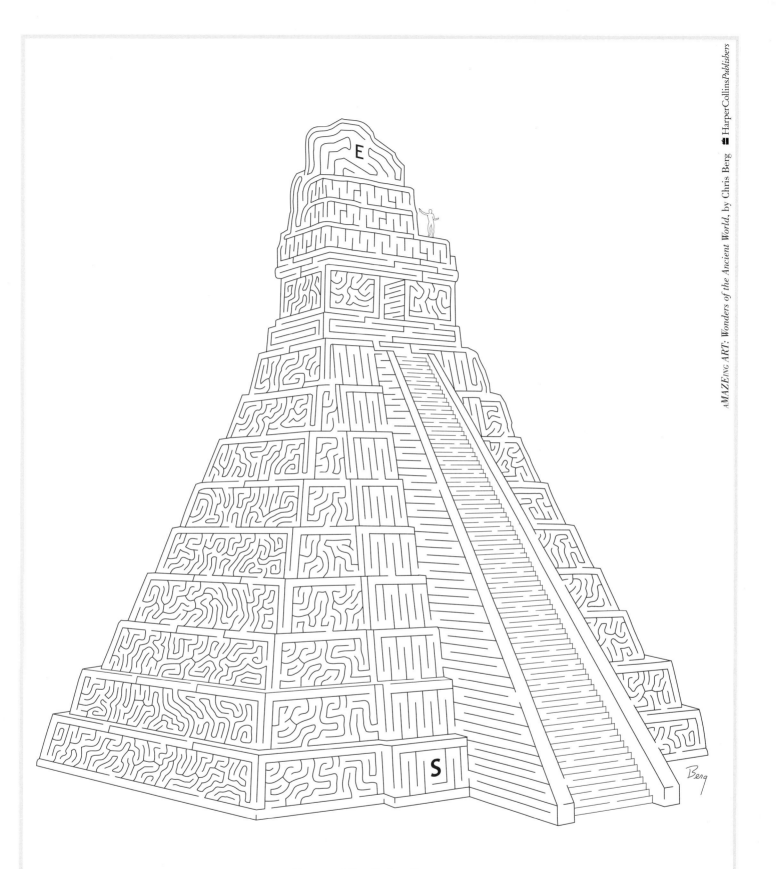

AMAZEing ART: Wonders of the Ancient World, by Chris Berg   HarperCollins*Publishers*

Pyramid of the Jaguar
Ancient Mayan Temple and Tomb
Tikal, Guatemala, Seventh Century A.D.

"We sat down on the very edge of the wall, and strove in vain to penetrate the mystery by which we were surrounded. Who were the people that built this city? In the ruined cities of Egypt, even in the long-lost Petra, the stranger knows the story of the people whose vestiges are around him. America, say historians, was peopled by savages; but savages never reared these structures, savages never carved these stones. We asked the Indians who made them, and their dull answer was '*Quien sabe?*'—'Who knows?'"

—JOHN LLOYD STEPHENS, EXPLORER AND TRAVEL WRITER, 1841

The most spectacular architectural achievements of the Maya are their many pyramids, which often cluster around large open plazas and probably belonged to ruling families. They were constructed from a solid core of rubble faced with cut stone, and were covered by a thick layer of stucco that was typically painted a dull blood red. The pyramids were both temples and tombs; at the city of Tikal, one of the largest and most influential Mayan cities, the 155-foot-high Temple of the Jaguar concealed a stone-lined tomb chamber containing the powerful ruler Au Cacaw ("Lord Chocolate Bean"). A narrow stone tube or "psychoduct" connected a room atop the pyramid with the tomb chamber below, allowing communication between the spirit of Lord Chocolate Bean and his living worshippers. Atop such pyramids Mayan nobility underwent ritual bloodletting and self-torture, for they believed that blood nourished the gods, and that without it, cosmic disorder would result. They pierced their tongues with stingray spines and passed strings bristling with thorns through the holes, or used obsidian blades to make deep wounds in their arms and legs. Often a human life was believed to be required, and the principal object of Mayan ritual warfare, which was timed to coincide with the appearance of the planet Venus, was to capture high-ranking nobles from other cities alive; they were then tortured, mutilated, and sacrificed to the gods in elaborate ceremonies designed to keep the cosmos running smoothly.

The Maya had many other strange, though less violent, customs and beliefs. According to their ideals of beauty, it was desirable to be cross-eyed, and to have triangular or notched teeth and an artificially flattened forehead. Thus Mayan aristocrats filed their teeth to points or packed them with bits of jade, attached small beads in front of their children's eyes to make them go cross-eyed, and tightly bound infants' heads to wooden boards. They believed that history repeated itself in endlessly recurrent cycles, and that the world had been destroyed four times already. Mayan prophesy seems to predict that the end of the current 5200-year "Great Cycle" of creation and destruction will occur on December 24, 2012, when the world will end with massive earthquakes and an overwhelming flood. Unfortunately the precise date of this impending catastrophe is somewhat uncertain, as the fanatical Spanish bishop Diego de Landa burned thousands of the ancient Mayan books during the Spanish conquest, and only three have survived.

"HIGH-POINTED NOSE, SLIT EYES, PIGEON BREAST, WOLF VOICE, AND TIGER HEART"

The Great Wall of China is one of the most ambitious and fantastic construction projects ever undertaken by mankind. Like a huge sprawling snake, it forms an unbroken barrier stretching across 1,680 miles of towering mountains, fertile plains, and rocky deserts. Including secondary walls at strategic passes and various loops and extensions, the Great Wall meanders for an astonishing total of 4,000 miles and includes over 20,000 fortified towers. In places its 30-foot-high gray ramparts fade into the distance as far as the eye can see in either direction, causing many visitors to wonder: What was it that the Chinese feared so much that they would erect so formidable a wall? Surprisingly, the common notion that aggressive barbarian hordes dwelling on the northern steppes—the Mongols, Huns, Manchus, and others—compelled the Chinese to build the wall in order to defend themselves is not really true.

The Great Wall is actually a general term used for many smaller border walls, frequently joined together, that were built at different periods in Chinese history. The earliest Great Wall was known as the "Wall of Ten Thousand Li" (a *li* is a third of a mile), and was created when Ch'in Shih-huang, the ruler of the small kingdom of Ch'in, conquered neighboring kingdoms in the third century B.C. and connected their border walls to form one long wall. To rule his vast territory—which he named China—Ch'in Shih-huang created a rigid and authoritarian state, complete with secret police and an informant system. A staggeringly repressive tyrant, he ordered all books on literature and history burned to discourage and eradicate undesirable thought, had hundreds of scholars who opposed him put to death, and even banned all discussions of the past. In his spare time he was obsessed with funding expeditions in search of magic mushrooms and the elixir of immortality. Kindly described by a contemporary historian as having a "high-pointed nose, slit eyes, pigeon breast, wolf

"The [Mongols] are a calamity for China only because they desperately need clothes and food . . . [the Mongol leader] desires goods and profit; if we give them he will be happy; if we reject him he will be resentful, and no doubt will raid the borders."

—LI HSIEN, IMPERIAL GRAND SECRETARY OF THE MING DYNASTY, 1459

109

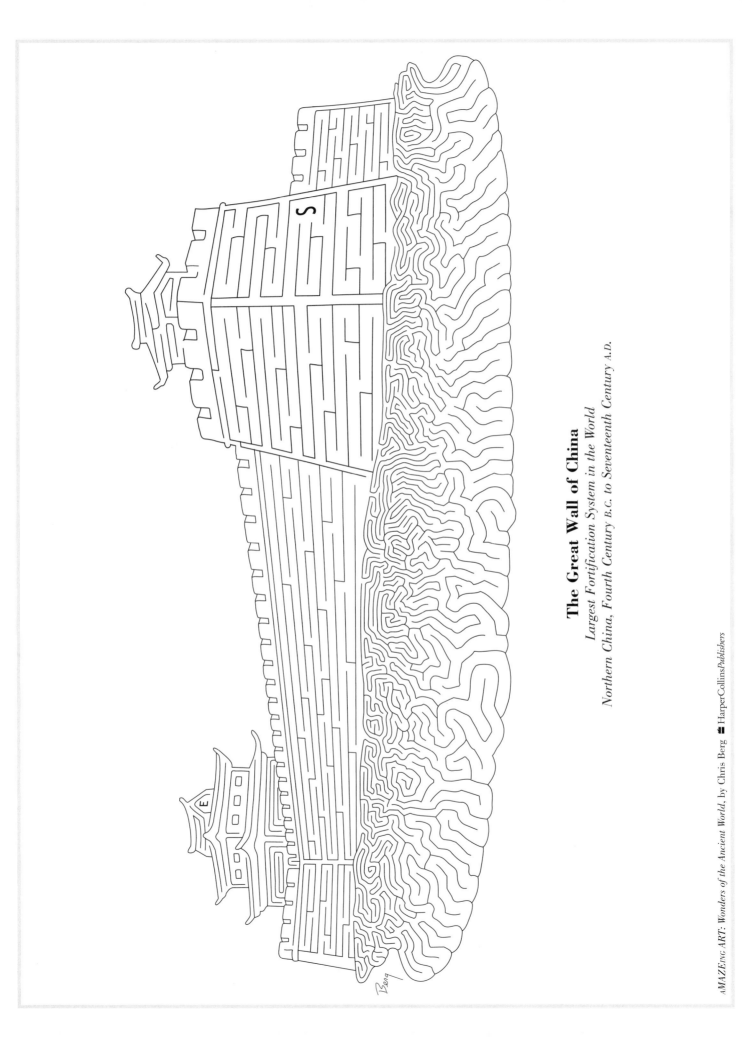

The Great Wall of China

Largest Fortification System in the World

Northern China, Fourth Century B.C. to Seventeenth Century A.D.

AMAZEing ART: Wonders of the Ancient World, by Chris Berg ▦ HarperCollins*Publishers*

voice, and tiger heart," he was such a despotic emperor that his own mother publicly denounced him.

The greatest threat to Ch'in Shih-huang's empire came not from the northern steppe-dwellers, who were weak and divided in his time, but rather from millions of unemployed and potentially rebellious Chinese peasants and intellectuals. The emperor's solution was simple: He enslaved his own citizens, keeping them busy laboring on enormous construction projects such as giant canals, opulent royal palaces, and the Wall of Ten Thousand Li. Hundreds of thousands of people, many of them scholars and political prisoners, died in the harsh working conditions prevalent on these projects. So many died along the wall that it became known as the "Longest Cemetery on Earth."

Most of Ch'in Shih-huang's wall was constructed out of tamped earth rather than stone, and very little of it has survived. Over the years later dynasties embarked on their own wall-building projects, and the present ruins of the Great Wall largely date from the cultured and sophisticated Ming Dynasty (1368–1644). In Ming times the northern steppe-dwellers were the Mongols, a nomadic and pastoral people who were fierce mounted warriors. The Ming Imperial Court, which was dominated by silk-robed eunuchs and southern literati, considered dealing with such "barbarians" demeaning. After all, the Mongols dwelt in the demon-infested north, rode horses and wore animal skins, and even practiced the shocking habit of eating cheese. They were held in such contempt that a Ming emperor once issued an official proclamation that the character for "barbarian" must always be written as small as possible! Wanting nothing to do with such people, the Ming withdrew from their northernmost territories, severing the centuries-old trading links that had existed along their border.

As it turned out, however, the Mongols were not entirely self-sufficient, and had to trade with the Chinese for the grain and the metal tools that they needed in order to survive. Mongol rulers were willing to accept a vassal status to the Ming Emperor in exchange for simple trade privileges, but the xenophobic Ming consistently refused their overtures—even during a year of famine in the north. Instead, the Ming put to death Mongol diplomatic envoys and sent a large army, headed by an inexperienced boy-emperor and his chief eunuch, deep into the northern steppes. When this army was soundly defeated by Mongol mounted warriors, the Ming embarked on a frenzy of defensive wall-building, straining their imperial treasuries and causing discontent among the peasants. The result was the Great Wall that survives today, perhaps the greatest monument to diplomatic incompetence in the world. At its peak it was defended by over one million soldiers, but like France's Maginot Line, it failed its only important test—it did not hold back the "barbarians" who soon put an end to the Ming dynasty.

"Of old the battles along the Great Wall
Were spoken of with lofty praise,
But antiquity has now been transformed to yellow dust.
White bones jumbled amongst the grass."

—WANG CH'ANG LING,
TANG DYNASTY POET

"What a great wall this is!"

—RICHARD NIXON,
1972

THE GIANTS
OF EASTER ISLAND

"These stone images
caused us to be struck
with astonishment,
because we could not
comprehend how it was
possible that these people
had been able to erect
such images."

—JACOB ROGGEVEEN,
DUTCH NAVAL
COMMANDER, EASTER
SUNDAY, 1722

Easter Island fascinates explorers of ancient mysteries as much as any place on earth, but in one of the ironies of history, the island was probably ignored by the first Europeans who sighted it. In 1687 wayward winds and ocean currents had pushed the English privateer Edward Davis 1,500 miles off course in the unexplored South Pacific. His crew sighted mountains on the horizon, but in what was surely one of the most unspirited decisions in the history of exploration, Captain Davis immediately swung his ship due east and set a course for Peru. He departed without making landfall or even learning whether he had discovered a small island or an entire continent.

Davis had likely seen what Dutch explorers, on Easter Sunday in 1722, would later name Easter Island. Had he taken the time to investigate, he would have been the first European to gaze upon the enormous brooding statues that are scattered over this small volcanic island lost in the expanse of the Pacific. Later explorers marveled at the size of these gaunt, monolithic figures with their elongated ears, jutting chins, and protuberant bellies. There are nearly a thousand of them, placed singly or in rows on raised platforms; along the coastline they were mounted to gaze inward to the center of the island. Made from a soft yellow-gray volcanic rock called tuff, the statues reach heights of up to 32 feet and can weigh as much as 80 tons. They were carved at an extraordinary quarry inside the slumbering volcano of Rano Raraku on the northeastern tip of the island, where hundreds of empty niches in the rock wall, and many abandoned unfinished stone figures, can be found.

The statues probably represent ancestral chiefs or spiritual leaders rather than gods. Their hands are placed across their bellies to protect ritual knowledge and oral traditions, which Pacific island cultures believed were stored in the belly. The islanders referred to them as Aringa Ora ("living faces"), and believed that they contained an energetic magic known as *mana* that protected their descendants. In 1722 Dutch explorers observed the early morning ceremonies in which the islanders worshipped these statues of their ancestors: they set fires before the stone images and

The Enigmatic Statues of Easter Island
Remotest Inhabited Island on Earth
South Pacific, 1000 to 1500 B.C.

aMAZEing ART: Wonders of the Ancient World, by Chris Berg ▪ HarperCollinsPublishers

then, sitting down on their heels with bowed heads, brought the palms of their hands together, moving them up and down.

Eighteenth-century European explorers all agreed that the primitive islanders, who eked out a meager living on sparse soil, appeared entirely incapable of having erected the statues. Captain Cook, who visited the island in 1774, wrote that he "could hardly conceive how these islanders, wholly unacquainted with any mechanical power, could raise such stupendous figures." Modern anthropologists agree with Cook's assessment: they have determined that the statues were erected between 1000 and 1500 A.D., when the unique Polynesian civilization that developed on Easter Island was at its height. Long before the first Europeans arrived, this civilization had collapsed due to an ecological disaster the islanders brought upon themselves.

Although it is barren and wind-swept today, Easter Island was once densely carpeted with forests of giant Chilean palm trees. The islanders began cutting down these trees around 750 A.D., probably to build canoes and to make the large wooden rollers or levers that were necessary for moving their giant statues. In addition, a type of Polynesian rat that the islanders cultivated for food ate the nuts of these trees, slowing their spread. By 1450 all the island's forests were gone. The rich volcanic soil began to erode into the ocean, croplands deteriorated, and the society disintegrated into anarchy. By the time Captain Cook arrived in 1774, warring kinship groups were destroying each other's statues, toppling them onto boulders that snapped their thin necks in two; very few remain standing today.

In addition to its enigmatic stone figures, Easter Island is well known for the 1947 voyage of the Kon Tiki. In a celebrated feat of daring, Thor Heyerdahl and his crew of five men and a parrot set sail from Peru for Easter Island on a primitive balsa log raft. The voyage was intended to substantiate Heyerdahl's theory—now known to be incorrect—that the Polynesians had originated in South America. For 101 days they drifted across 4,300 miles of open sea; although the parrot was washed overboard, the men eventually landed far to the west of Easter Island, near Tahiti.

> "[They] seemed to be triumphing over us, asking: 'Guess how this engineering work was done! Guess how we moved these gigantic figures down the steep walls of the volcano and carried them over the hills to any place on the island we liked!'"
>
> —THOR HEYERDAHL, ADVENTURER AND WRITER, 1950s

> "In Easter Island . . . the shadows of the departed builders still possess the land . . . the whole air vibrates with a vast purpose and energy which has been and is no more. What was it? Why was it?"
>
> —KATHERINE ROUTLEDGE, EXPLORER AND ARCHAEOLOGIST, 1920

LOST CITIES

AND

FORGOTTEN

EMPIRES

"It is a grand thing, but I feel a terror and a dread, lest someone should one day give the same order about my own native city." Thus spoke the Roman general Scipio in 146 B.C., after he had given an order to erase the city of Carthage from the face of the earth. In Scipio's time Carthage was one of the largest and richest cities in the world, and for more than a century, she fought a series of bitter wars with Rome over profitable Mediterranean trade routes. Carthage was ultimately defeated, its few surviving inhabitants were enslaved, and the city was then burned to the ground, leveled, and plowed over with salt by Roman legions so that it would be uninhabitable for future generations. Scipio wept when he saw Carthage perish so utterly, from an order he himself had given, and feared that his own city, Rome, might one day share the same terrible fate.

In one sense Carthage was lucky, for although almost nothing remains of this once-great city, its story was preserved in exquisite detail by Roman historians as they chronicled the rise of Rome. Other cities from the ancient world have not been so fortunate. The city of Akkad, which united all of Mesopotamia into one of the first great empires around 2300 B.C., has not even been located by archaeologists. It lies buried beneath the earth awaiting discovery, as does the capital of the Mitanni Empire, a great power that was once on equal footing with Egypt. And even though we have found the bastions of their impressive capital city at Gordium, we know very little about the Phrygians, who occupied Anatolia during a "dark age" in history. Their language is still enshrouded in mystery, and only two words of an inscription on the Midas Monument, the central object in an ancient Phrygian sacred enclosure, can be understood: *Midai Wanaktei*, meaning "Midas is Ruler." The rest of the script, which seems to be related to the early Phoenician and Greek alphabets, is a tantalizing puzzle. Our scant knowledge of Phrygian religion comes from the Romans, who in 204 B.C. had the sacred black meteorite of the Phrygian mother goddess, Cybele, brought to Rome along with Phrygian priests. Thus we at least know that the high priestess of Cybele was attended by a band of fanatical male acolytes called Galli, who castrated themselves in their ecstasy upon entering her service.

aMAZEing ART: Wonders of the Ancient World, by Chris Berg ■ HarperCollins*Publishers*

The Midas Monument
One of the few surviving remnants of a once-great Phrygian civilization
Near Gordium, Anatolia, Eighth Century B.C.

"For the sea was raised by an earthquake and it submerged Helike, and also the Temple of Elikonian Poseidon . . . Erastothenes says that he himself saw the place, and that the ferrymen say that there was a bronze Poseidon in the strait, standing erect, holding a hippocamp in his hand, which was perilous for those who fished with nets. The submersion took place by night . . . and although the city was 12 stadia distant from the sea, this whole district together with the city was submerged."

—STRABO, GREEK GEOGRAPHER, FIRST CENTURY B.C.

Some lost cities from antiquity were the victims of spectacular natural disasters. Pompei and Herculaneum, entombed beneath 20 feet of volcanic ash from the eruption of Mt. Vesuvius in 79 A.D., are perhaps the most famous, but they are hardly alone. Helike, once an important Greek city, was destroyed and submerged in the middle of the night by a great earthquake and seismic sea wave in 373 B.C. Two thousand men sent by neighboring cities were unable to recover any victims; only Helike's giant bronze statue of Poseidon—the god of the sea and of earthquakes—was left standing alone in the watery strait. The rich and luxuriant Egyptian cities of Canopus and Menouthis, covered over by the Mediterranean Sea following an earthquake, shared the same fate.

Evidence is accumulating that the demise of numerous cities, previously believed to be isolated events, may in some cases have been part of major global geologic and climatic upheavals. One of the most severe of these upheavals occurred around 2300 B.C. in the early Bronze Age. At this time in Egypt the level of the Nile dropped dramatically, plunging the country into anarchy and bringing the age of the great pyramid builders to an end. In Syria rich farmland turned to windblown dust, and many cities were overthrown by earthquakes. In the Sahara region of North Africa, rainfall ceased and rivers dried up, turning a once green and fertile land into the uninhabitable desert it is today. It was also around 2300 B.C. that Sodom and Gomorrah, the biblical cities guilty of unspecified depravity, were destroyed by massive seismic upheavals and uncontrollable fires. The most intriguing theory capable of explaining such diverse catastrophes postulates the impact of a comet or cometary fragments upon the earth; dust thrown into the atmosphere would cause severe climate change, and the shock from the impact(s) would cause massive earthquakes worldwide. Bronze Age texts are actually full of references to gods raining fire down from the skies, and in the Bible the destruction of Sodom and Gomorrah was itself attributed to "fire from heaven."

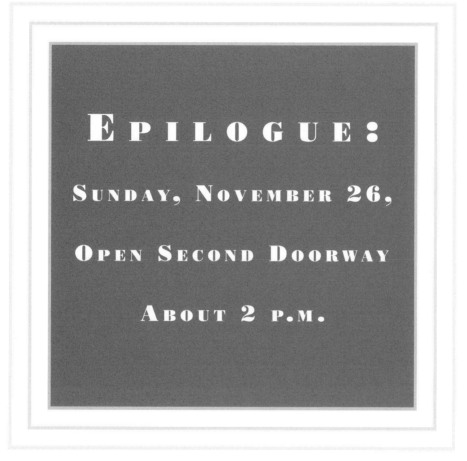

EPILOGUE:

SUNDAY, NOVEMBER 26,

OPEN SECOND DOORWAY

ABOUT 2 P.M.

Feverishly we cleared away the remaining last scraps of rubbish on the floor of the passage, until we had only the clean sealed doorway before us. After making preliminary notes, we made a tiny breach in the top left-hand corner to see what was beyond. Darkness and the iron testing rod told us that there was empty space. Perhaps another descending staircase, in accordance to the ordinary royal Theban tomb plan? Or maybe a chamber? Candles were procured—the all important tell-tale for foul gases when opening an ancient subterranean excavation—and I widened the breach and by means of the candle looked in, while Ld. C., Lady E., and Callender with the Reises waited in anxious expectation.

"It was sometime before I could see, the hot air escaping caused the candle to flicker, but as soon as my eyes became accustomed to the glimmer of light the interior of the chamber gradually loomed before me, with its strange and wonderful medley of extraordinary and beautiful objects heaped upon one another.

"There was naturally short suspense for those present who could not see, when Lord Carnarvon said to me 'Can you see anything?' I replied to him 'Yes, it is wonderful.' I then with precaution made the hole sufficiently large for both of us to see. With the light of an electric torch as well as an additional candle we looked in. Our sensations and astonishment are difficult to describe as the better light revealed to us the marvelous collection of treasures: two strange ebony-black effigies of a King, gold-sandalled, bearing staff and mace, loomed out from the cloak of darkness; gilded couches in strange forms, lion-headed, Hathor-headed, and beast infernal; exquisitely painted, inlaid, and ornamental caskets; alabaster vases, some beautifully executed of lotus and papyrus device; strange black shrines, with a gilded monster snake appearing from within; quite ordinary looking white chests; finely carved chairs; a golden inlaid throne; beneath our very eyes, on the threshold, a lovely lotiform wishing-cup in translucent alabaster; and, lastly, a confusion of overturned parts of chariots glinting with gold, peering from amongst which was a mannequin. The first impression suggested the property-room of an opera of a vanished civilization. Our sensations were bewildering and full of strange emotion. We questioned one another as to the meaning of it all. Was it a tomb or merely a cache? A sealed doorway between the two sentinel statues proved there was more beyond, and with the numerous cartouches bearing the name of Tut.ankh.Amun on most of the objects before us, there was little doubt that there behind was the grave of that Pharaoh."

Diary entry of Howard Carter, Sunday, November 26, 1922, [edited] describing the opening of Tutankhamun's tomb, one of the most significant finds in the history of archaeology.

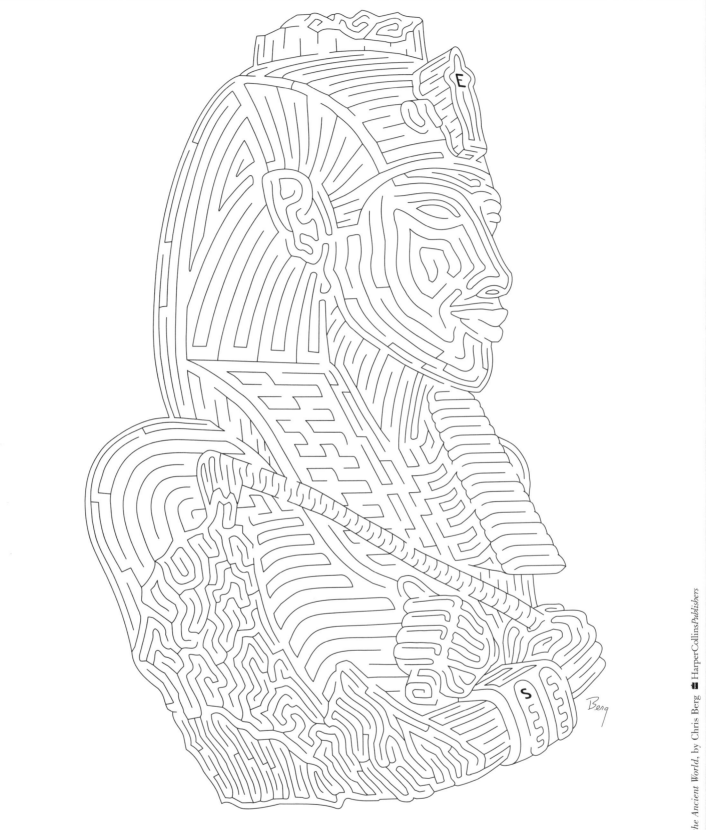

The Past Reclaimed
Colossal Stone Sculpture of Akhenaton
Predecessor of Tutankhamun
Karnak, Egypt, 1350 B.C.

aMAZEing ART: Wonders of the Ancient World, by Chris Berg, HarperCollinsPublishers

SOLUTIONS
TO THE LABYRINTH PUZZLES

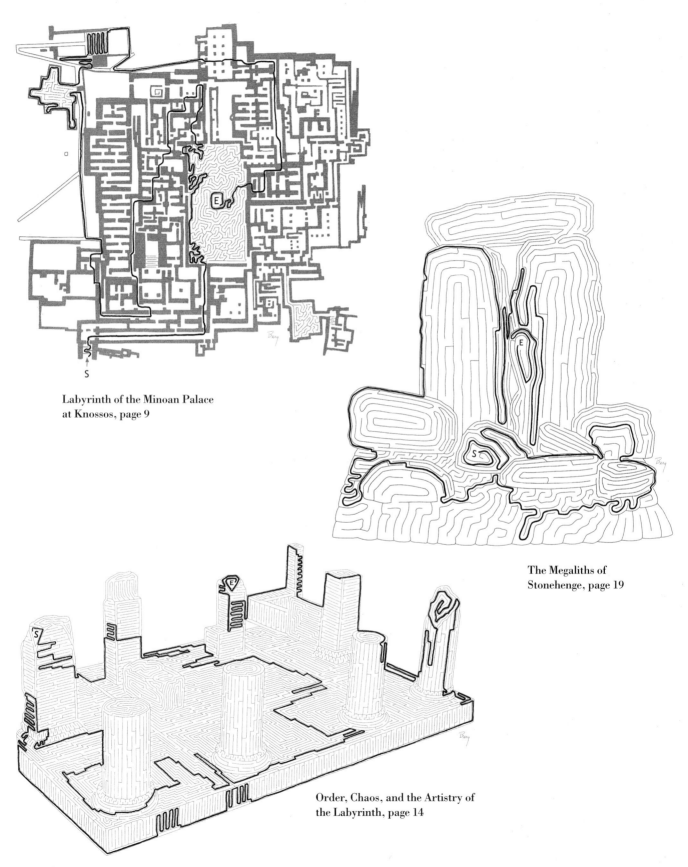

Labyrinth of the Minoan Palace
at Knossos, page 9

The Megaliths of
Stonehenge, page 19

Order, Chaos, and the Artistry of
the Labyrinth, page 14

AMAZEing ART: Wonders of the Ancient World, by Chris Berg ■ HarperCollins*Publishers*

Ggantija and the Megalithic
Temples on Malta, page 22

The Temple of Amun at
Karnak, page 32

The Pyramids at Gîza, page 26

The Riddle of the Sphinx,
page 29

123

AMAZEing ART: Wonders of the Ancient World, by Chris Berg ▉ HarperCollinsPublishers

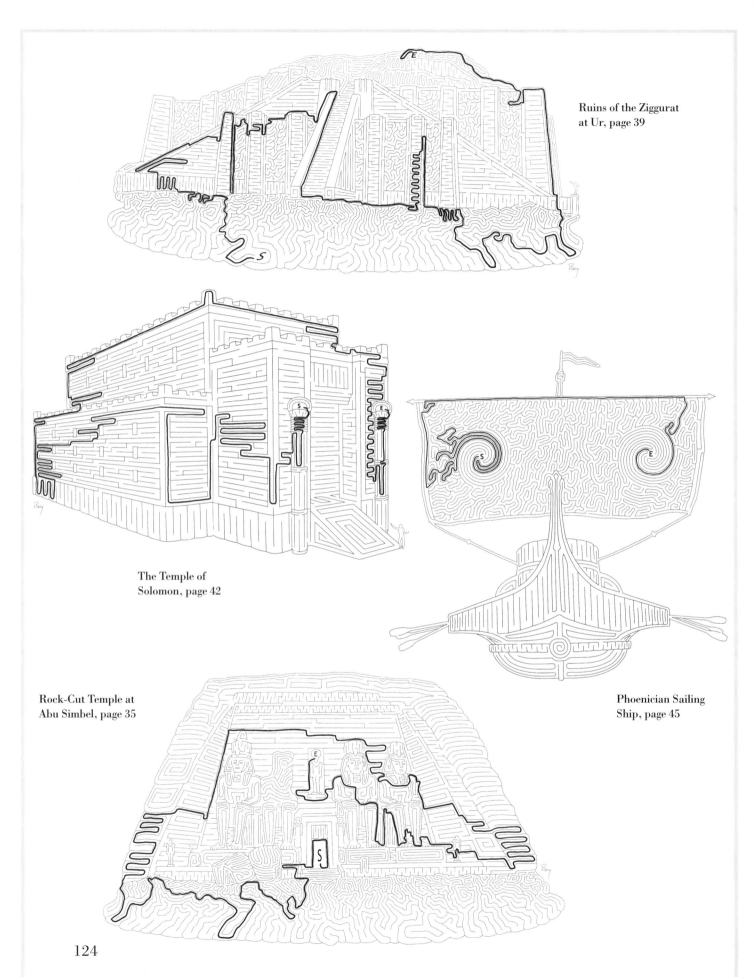

Ruins of the Ziggurat
at Ur, page 39

The Temple of
Solomon, page 42

Phoenician Sailing
Ship, page 45

Rock-Cut Temple at
Abu Simbel, page 35

124

AMAZEING ART: Wonders of the Ancient World, by Chris Berg ■ HarperCollins*Publishers*

The Hanging Gardens,
page 51

Winged Guardian Bull
(Lamassu), page 48

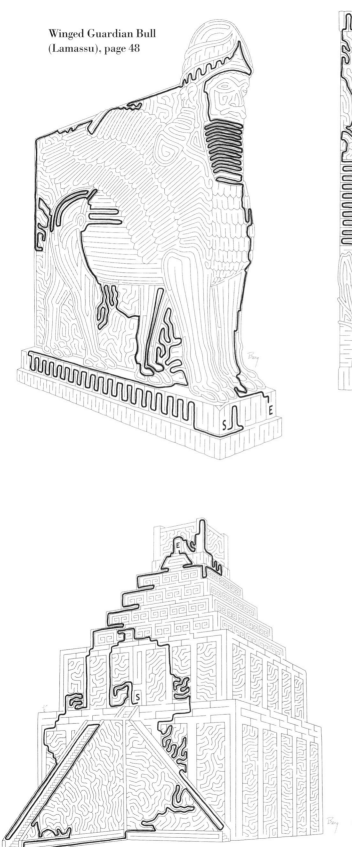

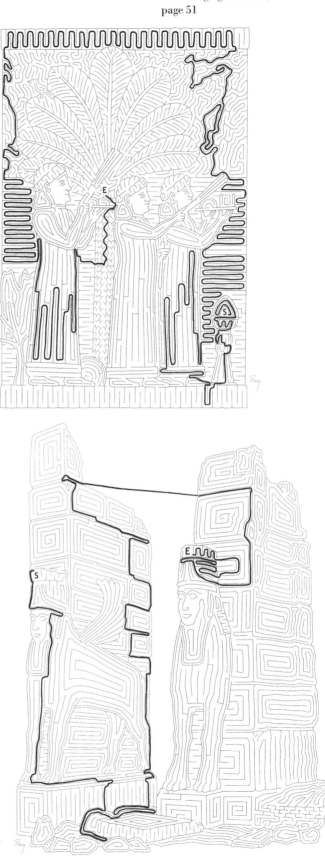

The Ziggurat of Marduk at
Babylon, page 54

Ruins of the Gate of
Xerxes, page 57

125

AMAZEing ART: Wonders of the Ancient World, by Chris Berg ✚ HarperCollinsPublishers

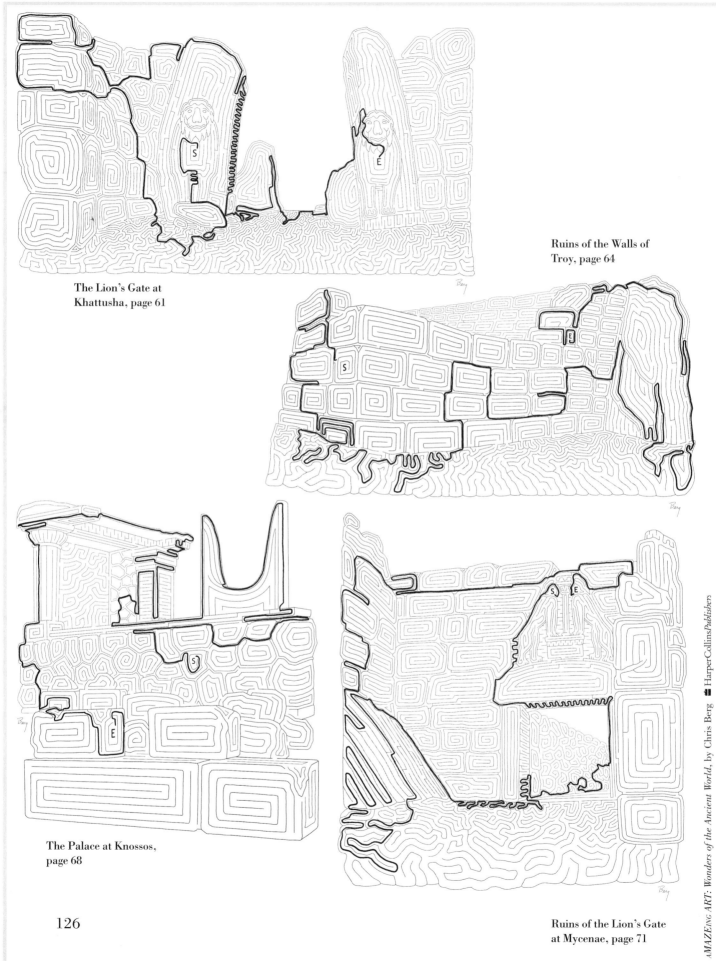

The Lion's Gate at
Khattusha, page 61

Ruins of the Walls of
Troy, page 64

The Palace at Knossos,
page 68

Ruins of the Lion's Gate
at Mycenae, page 71

126

AMAZEING ART: Wonders of the Ancient World, by Chris Berg ■ HarperCollins Publishers

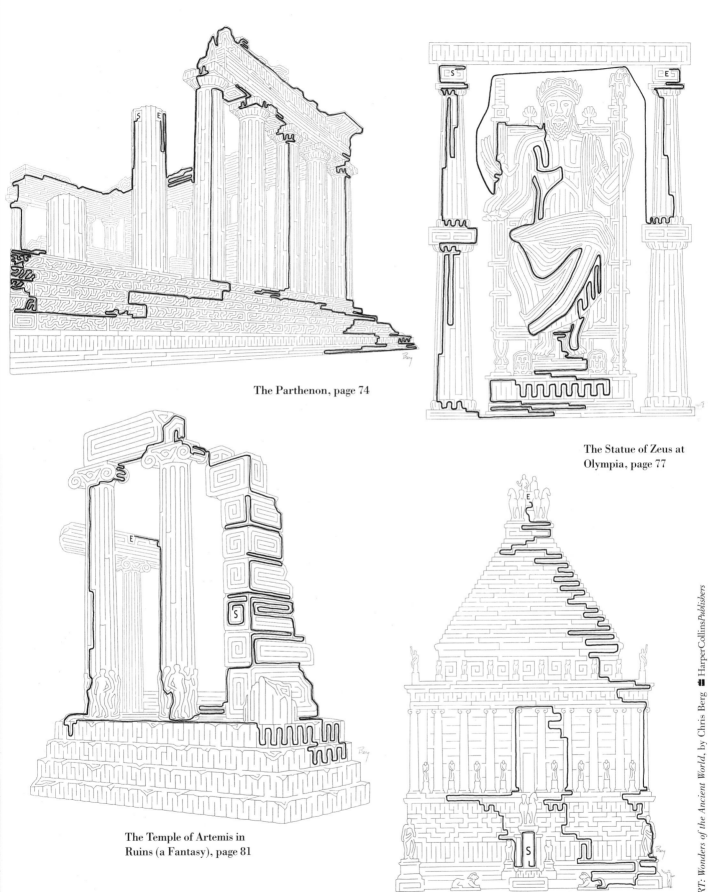

The Parthenon, page 74

The Statue of Zeus at
Olympia, page 77

The Temple of Artemis in
Ruins (a Fantasy), page 81

The Mausoleum at
Halicarnassus, page 84

127

AMAZEING ART: Wonders of the Ancient World, by Chris Berg ▪ HarperCollinsPublishers

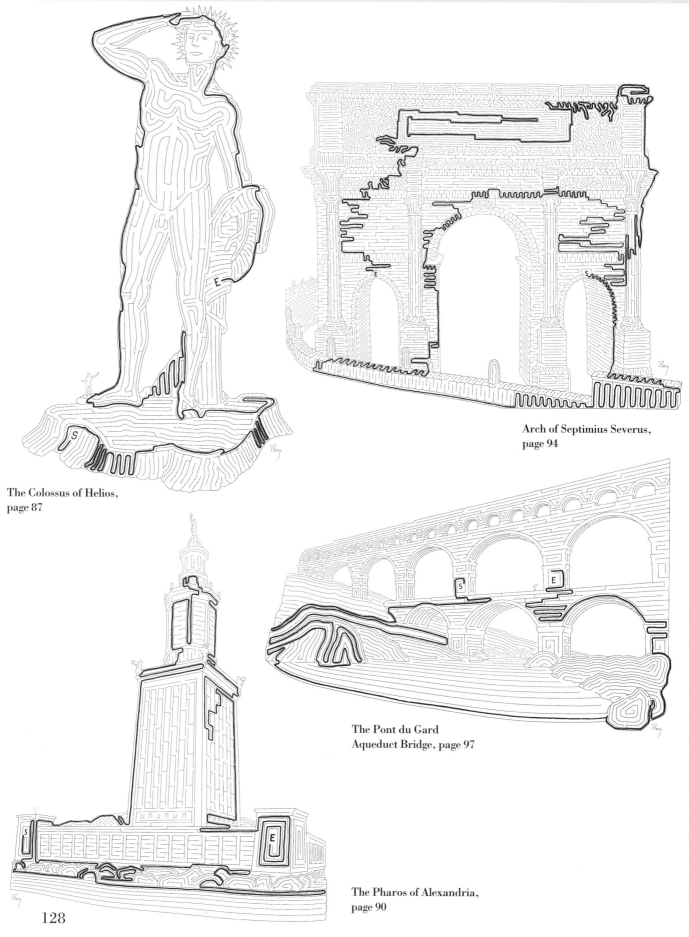

The Colossus of Helios,
page 87

Arch of Septimius Severus,
page 94

The Pont du Gard
Aqueduct Bridge, page 97

The Pharos of Alexandria,
page 90

128

*A*MAZE*ing ART: Wonders of the Ancient World*, by Chris Berg ☖ *HarperCollinsPublishers*

Pyramid of the Jaguar,
page 107

The Interior of the
Pantheon, page 103

Ruins of the Colosseum,
page 100

The Great Wall of China,
page 110

AMAZEing ART: Wonders of the Ancient World, by Chris Berg **ﬂ** HarperCollins*Publishers*

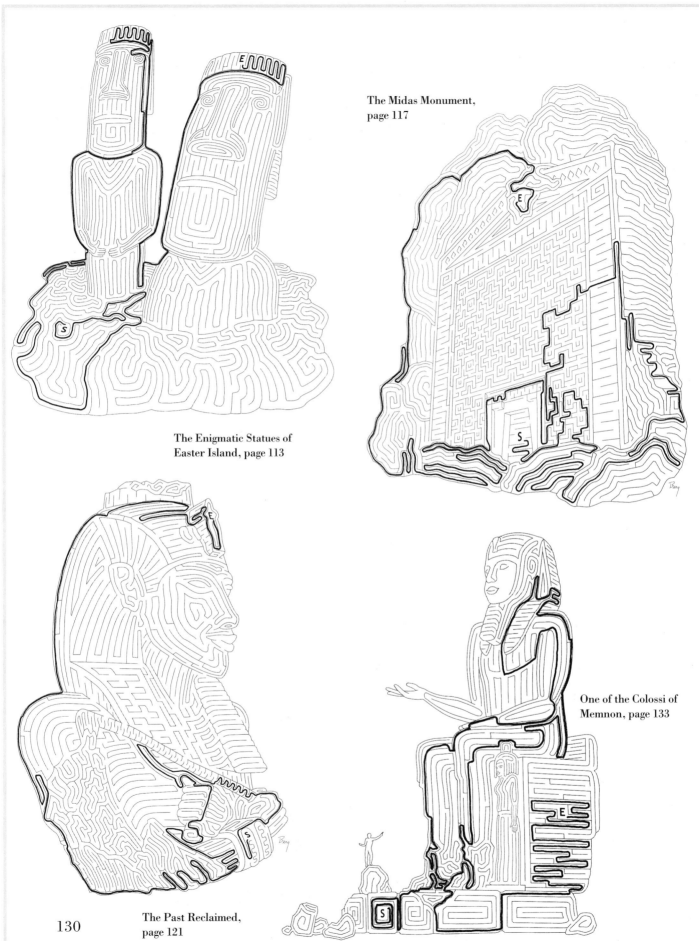

The Midas Monument,
page 117

The Enigmatic Statues of
Easter Island, page 113

One of the Colossi of
Memnon, page 133

The Past Reclaimed,
page 121

130

AMAZEing ART: Wonders of the Ancient World, by Chris Berg ▦ HarperCollins*Publishers*

FURTHER READING

Mazes and Labyrinths

Artress, Lauren, *Walking a Sacred Path* (New York: Riverhead Books, 1995)

Doob, Penelope, *The Idea of the Labyrinth* (Ithaca: Cornell University Press, 1990)

Fisher, Adrian, *Secrets of the Maze* (London: Barron's Educational Series, 1997)

Jaskolski, Helmut, *The Labyrinth: Symbol of Fear, Rebirth, and Liberation* (Boston: Shambhala, 1997)

Kern, Hermann, *Through the Labyrinth: Designs and Meanings over 5,000 Years* (New York: Prestel, 2000)

Matthews, W. H., *Mazes and Labyrinths, Their History and Development* (New York: Dover, 1970)

Pennick, Nigel, *Mazes and Labyrinths* (London: Robert Hale, 1990)

The Ancient World: General Reading

Bahn, Paul G., *The Cambridge Illustrated History of Archaeology* (New York: Cambridge University Press, 1996)

Barnes, M., et al., *Secrets of Lost Empires* (London: Sterling Publications, 1996)

Cantor, Norman F., *Civilization of the Ancient World* (New York: HarperCollins, 2001)

Clayton, P., and M. Price (eds.), *The Seven Wonders of the Ancient World* (London, 1988)

Connolly, Peter, and Hazel Dodge, *The Ancient City, Life in Classical Athens and Rome* (Oxford: Oxford University Press, 1998)

De Camp, L. Sprague, *The Ancient Engineers* (New York: Ballentine, 1988)

Eydoux, Henri-Paul, *In Search of Lost Worlds* (New York: Hamlyn, 1971)

Freeman, Charles, *Egypt, Greece and Rome* (Oxford: Oxford University Press, 1996)

James, Peter, and Nick Thorpe, *Ancient Mysteries* (New York: Ballentine, 1999)

Kostof, Spiro, *A History of Architecture* (Oxford: Oxford University Press, 1995)

Kuhrt, Emelie, *The Ancient Near East* (New York: Routledge, 1997)

Lloyd, S., et al., *Ancient Architecture: Mesopotamia, Egypt, Crete, and Greece* (New York: Harry N. Abrams, 1974)

Pomeroy, S., *Goddesses, Whores, Wives, and Slaves: Women in Classical Antiquity* (New York: Schocken, 1975)

Romer, J., and E. Romer, *The Seven Wonders of the World* (London: Seven Dials, 1995)

Sasson, Jack M. (ed.), *Civilizations of the Ancient Near East* (2 vol. encyclopedia) (New York: Hendrickson, 2001)

Scarre, Chris (ed.), *Seventy Wonders of the Ancient World* (London: Thames & Hudson, 1999)

Snell, Daniel, *Life in the Ancient Near East* (New Haven: Yale University Press, 1997)

Zinsser, Hans, *Rats, Lice and History* (Boston: Little, Brown, 1935)

The Ancient Civilizations

THE MEGALITH BUILDERS
(LABYRINTHS: STONEHENGE AND TEMPLES AT MALTA)

Burl, A., *Great Stone Circles: Fables, Fictions, Facts* (New Haven: Yale University Press, 1999)

Chippindale, C., *Stonehenge Complete* (New York: Thames & Hudson, 1994)

Cunliffe, Barry (ed.), *Prehistoric Europe, an Illustrated History* (Oxford: Oxford University Press, 1994)

Evans, J. D., *The Prehistoric Antiquities of the Maltese Islands* (London: Athlone Press, 1971)

Hawkins, G. S., *Stonehenge Decoded* (New York: Dell, 1965)

Mohen, J.-P., *The World of Megaliths* (New York: Facts on File, 1989)

O'Kelly, M., *Newgrange: Archaeology, Art and Legend* (London: Thames & Hudson, 1995)

Rudgley, Richard, *Lost Civilizations of the Stone Age* (New York: Simon & Schuster, 1999)

SUMER
(LABYRINTH: ZIGGURAT AT UR)

Crawford, H., *Sumer and the Sumerians* (New York: Cambridge University Press, 1991)

Kramer, Samuel Noah, *History Begins at Sumer: Thirty-nine Firsts in Man's Recorded History* (Philadelphia: University of Pennsylvania Press, 1981)

Oppenheim, Leo, and Erica Remer, *Ancient Mesopotamia: Portrait of a Dead Civilization* (Chicago: University of Chicago Press, 1997)

Postgate, J. N., *Early Mesopotamia, Society and Economy at the Dawn of History* (New York: Routledge, 1992)

Roaf, Michael, *The Cultural Atlas of Mesopotamia and the Ancient Near East* (New York: Facts on File, 1990)

EGYPT
(LABYRINTHS: PYRAMIDS, SPHINX, TEMPLES AT KARNAK, ABU SIMBEL, AND COLOSSI OF AKHENATEN)

Adkins, Lesley, and Roy Adkins, *The Keys of Egypt: The Obsession to Decipher Egyptian Hieroglyphs* (New York: HarperCollins, 2000)

Aldred, Cyril, *The Egyptians* (London: Thames & Hudson, 1998)

Arnold, D., *Building in Egypt: Pharaonic Stone Masonry* (Oxford: Oxford University Press, 1997)

Baines, John, and Jaromir Malek, *A Cultural Atlas of Ancient Egypt* (New York: Facts on File, 2000)

Bradford, Ernle, *Cleopatra* (New York: Penguin, 2001)

Brier, Bob, *Egyptian Mummies: Unraveling the Secrets of an Ancient Art* (New York: Quill, 1996)

Clayton, Peter, *The Rediscovery of Ancient Egypt* (London: Portland, 1982)

David, Rosalie, and Rick Archbold, *Conversations With Mummies: New Light on the Lives of Ancient Egyptians* (New York: HarperCollins, 2000)

Davies, V., and R. Friedman, *Egypt Uncovered* (New York: Stewart Tabori & Chang, 1988)

Hawass, Zahi, *Silent Images, Women in Pharaonic Egypt* (New York: Harry N. Abrams, 2000)

Hobson, Christine, *The World of the Pharaohs* (New York: Thames & Hudson, 1998)

Hughes-Hallett, Lucy, *Cleopatra: Histories, Dreams and Distortions* (New York: HarperCollins Publishers, 1991)

Johnson, Paul, *The Civilization of Ancient Egypt* (New York: HarperCollins, 1999)

Kaster, J., *The Literature and Mythology of Ancient Egypt* (London: Allen Lane, 1970)

Lehner, M., *The Complete Pyramids* (New York: Thames & Hudson, 1997)

Lichtheim, M., *Ancient Egyptian Literature, A Book of Readings* (Berkeley: University of California Press, 1980)

MacQuitty, W., *Abu Simbel* (New York: Putnam, 1965)

Malek, J., *Egyptian Art* (London: Phaidon Press, 1999)

McMahan, Ian, *Secrets of the Pharaohs* (New York: Avon, 1998)

Mendelssohn, K., *The Riddle of the Pyramids* (London: W. W. Norton, 1974)

Morkot, R. G., *The Black Pharaohs: Egypt's Nubian Rulers* (London: Rubicon, 2000)

O'Connor, D. B., *Ancient Nubia: Egypt's Rival in Africa* (Philadelphia: University of Pennsylvania, 1993)

Quirke, S., *Ancient Egyptian Religion* (New York: Dover, 1993)

Robins, G., *Women in Ancient Egypt* (Cambridge, MA: Harvard University Press, 1993)

Schultz, R., and M. Seidel, *Egypt: The World of the Pharaohs* (Cologne: Konemann, 1998)

Silverman, D. (ed.), *Ancient Egypt* (New York: Oxford University Press, 1997)

Smith, W. S., *The Art and Architecture of Ancient Egypt* (New Haven: Yale University Press, 1999)

Weeks, K. R. (ed.), *The Lost Tomb: This Is His Incredible Story of Kv5 and Its Excavation* (New York: Quill, 1999)

ANATOLIA: TROY, THE HITTITES, AND THE PHRYGIANS
(LABYRINTHS: LION GATE AT HATTUSAS, WALLS OF TROY, AND MIDAS MONUMENT)

Blegen, C., *Troy and the Trojans* (London: Thames & Hudson, 1963)

Gurney, O. R., *The Hittites* (Baltimore: Penguin, 1966)

Luce, J. V., *Celebrating Homer's Landscapes: Troy and Ithaca Revisited* (New Haven: Yale University Press, 1998)

MacQueen, J. G., *The Hittites and Their Contempories in Asia Minor* (New York: Thames & Hudson, 1996)

Traill, David A., *Schliemann of Troy, Treasure and Deceit* (New York: St. Martin's Press, 1995)

Wood, Michael, *In Search of the Trojan War* (Berkeley: University of California Press, 1998)

BRONZE AGE GREECE
(LABYRINTHS: LION GATE AT MYCENAE AND PALACE OF KNOSSOS)

Higgins, R., *Minoans and Mycenaean Art* (London: Thames & Hudson, 1997)

Mylonas, G. E., *Mycenae and the Mycenaean Age* (Princeton: Princeton University Press, 1966)

Preziosi, D., and Hitchcock, L. A., *Aegean Art and Architecture* (New York: Oxford University Press, 2000)

Taylour, W. D., *The Mycenaeans* (New York: W. W. Norton, 1983)

Vermeule, Emily, *Greece in the Bronze Age* (Chicago: University of Chicago Press, 1972)

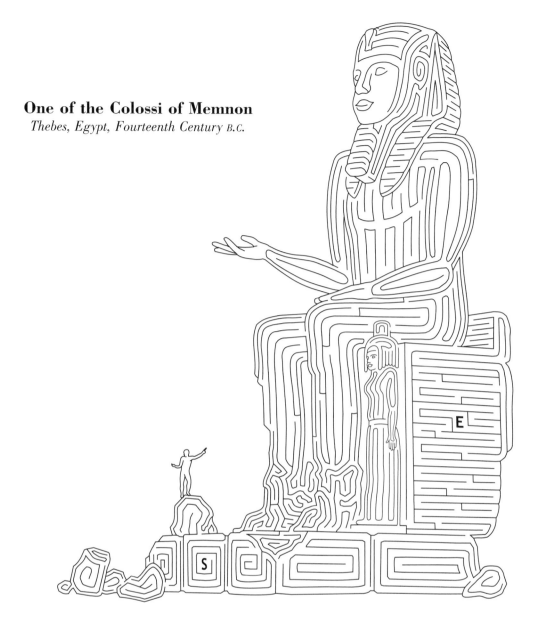

One of the Colossi of Memnon
Thebes, Egypt, Fourteenth Century B.C.

PHOENICIA AND ISRAEL
(LABYRINTHS: PHOENICIAN SHIP AND SOLOMON'S TEMPLE)

Avi-Yonah, M., *The Jews under Roman and Byzantine Rule* (New York: Schocken, 1984)

Casson, Lionel, *The Ancient Mariners* (Princeton: Princeton University Press, 1991)

Kamm, Antony, *The Israelites, an Introduction* (New York: Routledge, 1999)

Markoe, G., *Phoenicians* (Berkeley: University of California Press, 2001)

Moscati, S., *The World of the Phoenicians* (New York: Rizzoli, 2000)

Redford, D. B., *Egypt, Caanan and Israel in Ancient Times* (Princeton: Princeton University Press, 1993)

BABYLONIA, PERSIA, AND ASSYRIA
(LABYRINTHS: ASHURNASIRPAL'S LAMMASSU, ZIGGURAT OF MARDUK, AND GATE OF XERXES)

Curtis, J., *Ancient Persia* (Cambridge, MA: Harvard University Press, 1990)

Larsen, Mogens, *The Conquest of Assyria* (New York: Routledge, 1994)

Oates, J., *Babylon* (New York: Thames & Hudson, 1986)

Saggs, H. W. F., *Babylonians* (Berkeley: University of California Press, 2000)

———. *The Might That Was Assyria* (London: Sidgwick & Jackson, 1984)

GREECE

(LABYRINTHS: PARTHENON, STATUE OF ZEUS, MAUSOLEUM, TEMPLE OF ARTEMIS, PHAROS OF ALEXANDRIA, AND COLOSSUS OF RHODES)

Boardman, J., *The Greeks Overseas* (New York: Thames & Hudson, 1999)

Boardman, John, *Greek Art* (New York: Thames & Hudson, 1996)

Boardman, John et al. (eds.), *Greece and the Hellenistic World* (New York: Oxford University Press, 1988)

Bosworth, A. B., *Conquest and Empire: The Reign of Alexander the Great* (New York: Cambridge University Press, 1993)

Burkhardt, Jacob, *The Greeks and Greek Civilization* (New York: Griffin, 1999)

Burn, A. R., *The Penguin History of Greece* (New York: Penguin, 1990)

Bury, J. B., and Meiggs, Russell, *A History of Greece* (New York: St. Martin's Press, 1975)

Coulton, J., *Ancient Greek Architects at Work: Problems of Structure and Design* (Ithaca: Cornell University Press, 1982)

Davidson, James, *Courtesans and Fishcakes: The Consuming Passions of Classical Athens* (New York: HarperCollins, 1999)

Davies, J., *Democracy and Classical Greece* (Cambridge, MA: Harvard University Press, 1993)

Empereur, J.-Y., *Alexandria Rediscovered* (New York: George Braziller, 1998)

Finley, M. I., *The Ancient Greeks* (New York: Viking Press, 1992)

Golden, M., *Sport and Society in Ancient Greece* (Cambridge, U.K.: Cambridge University Press, 1998)

Green, Peter, *Alexander of Macedon* (Berkeley: University of California Press, 1992)

Guthrie, W. K. C., *The Greek Philosophers from Thales to Aristotle* (New York: HarperCollins, 1986)

Keeley, E., *Cavafy's Alexandria* (Princeton: Princeton University Press, 1995)

Levi, P., *Atlas of the Greek World* (New York: Facts on File, 1983)

Mills, Dorothy, *The Book of the Ancient Greeks* (New York: Putnam, 1925)

Murray, O., *Early Greece* (Cambridge, MA: Harvard University Press, 1993)

Pollit, J. J., *Art and Experience in Classical Greece* (Cambridge U.K.: Cambridge University Press, 1972)

Pomeroy, Sarah B., et al., *Ancient Greece, a Political, Social, and Cultural History* (New York: Oxford University Press, 1998)

Rhodes, R. F., *Architecture and Meaning on the Athenian Acropolis* (New York: Cambridge University Press, 1995)

Sowerby, R., *The Greeks: An Introduction to Their Culture* (New York: Routledge, 1995)

Stierlin, Henri, *Greece from Mycenae to the Parthenon* (Koln: Taschen, 1997)

Swaddling, J., *The Ancient Olympic Games* (Austin: University of Texas Press, 1984)

Tournikiotis, P., *The Parthenon and Its Impact on Modern Times* (New York: Harry N. Abrams, 1996)

Vernant, J.-P., *Myth and Society in Ancient Greece* (New York: Zone Books, 1988)

ROME

(LABYRINTHS: COLOSSEUM, ROMAN FORUM, PONT DU GARD AQUEDUCT, AND PANTHEON)

Bergmann, B., and C. Kondoleon (eds.), *The Art of Ancient Spectacle* (New Haven: Yale University Press, 2000)

Birley, A., *Hadrian: The Restless Emperor* (New York: Routledge, 2000)

———. *Septimius Severus* (New York: Routledge, 1999)

Boardman, J., Griffin, J., and O. Murray (eds.), *The Oxford Illustrated History of the Roman World* (New York: Oxford University Press, 2001)

Cornell, T., and J. Matthews, *Atlas of the Roman World* (New York: Facts on File, 1983)

Crawford, M., *The Roman Republic* (Cambridge, MA: Harvard University Press, 1993)

Dupont, F., *Daily Life in Ancient Rome* (Oxford: Blackwell, 1994)

Fagan, G., *Bathing in Public in the Roman World* (Ann Arbor: University of Michigan Press, 1999)

Henig, M. (ed.), *A Handbook of Roman Art: A Comprehensive Survey of All the Arts of the Roman World* (New York: Phaidon, 1995)

Hodge, A. T., *Roman Aqueducts and Water Supply* (London: Duckworth, 1992)

Kleiner, D., and S. B. Matheson (eds.), *I, Claudia: Women in Ancient Rome* (Austin: University of Texas Press, 1996)

Le Glay, et al., *A History of Rome* (Oxford: Blackwell Publishers, 2000)

Ling, R., *Roman Painting* (New York: Cambridge University Press, 1991)

MacDonald, W. I., *The Architecture of the Roman Empire: An Urban Appraisal* (New Haven: Yale University Press, 1988)

MacKendrick, P. L., *The Mute Stones Speak: The Story of Archaeology in Italy* (New York: W. W. Norton, 1983)

Meier, Christian, *Caesar* (New York: HarperCollins, 1997)

Scarre, C., *Chronicle of the Roman Emperors: The Reign-By-Reign Record of the Rulers of Imperial Rome* (New York: Thames & Hudson, 1995)

Shelton, J., *As the Romans Did: A Sourcebook in Roman Social History* (New York: Oxford University Press, 1998)

Southern, P., *Augustus* (New York: Routledge, 1998)

Stambaugh, J., *The Ancient Roman City* (Baltimore: Johns Hopkins University Press, 1988)

Strong, D., et al., *Roman Art* (New Haven: Yale University Press, 1992)

Veyne, Paul, *The Roman Empire* (Cambridge, MA: Belknap Press, 1997)

Ward-Perkins, J. B., *Roman Imperial Architecture* (New Haven: Yale University Press, 1992)

Wells, C., *The Roman Empire* (Cambridge, MA: Harvard University Press, 1995)

Wiedemann, Thomas, *Emperors and Gladiators* (New York: Routledge, 1995)

MESOAMERICA
(LABYRINTH: PYRAMID OF THE JAGUAR AT TIKAL)

Abrams, E., *How the Maya Built Their World* (Austin: University of Texas Press, 1994)

Coe, Michael, *The Maya* (New York: Thames & Hudson, 1999)

Gallenkamp, Charles, *Maya: The Riddle and Rediscovery of a Lost Civilization* (New York: Penguin, 1987)

Longhena, Maria, *Ancient Mexico: History and Culture of the Maya* (New York: Stewart, Tabori & Chang, 1998)

Pohl, John, *Exploring MesoAmerica* (New York: Oxford University Press, 1999)

Schele, Linda, and David Freidel, *A Forest of Kings: The Untold Story of the Ancient Maya* (New York: Quill, 1992)

Sharer, Robert, *The Ancient Maya* (Stanford: Stanford University Press, 1994)

PACIFIC ISLANDS
(LABYRINTH: EASTER ISLAND STATUES)

Bahn, Paul, and John Flenley, *Easter Island, Earth Island* (New York: Thames & Hudson, 1992)

Orliac, C., and M. Orliac, *Easter Island: Mystery of the Stone Giants* (New York: Harry N. Abrams, 1995)

CHINA
(LABYRINTH: GREAT WALL)

Fairbank, John, and Merle Goldman, *China: A New History* (Cambridge, MA: Harvard University Press, 1998)

Lum, Peter, *The Purple Barrier* (London: R. Hale, 1960)

Waldron, Arthur, *The Great Wall of China: From History to Myth* (New York: Cambridge University Press, 1992)

The Ancient Authors

Herodotus, *The Histories*, translated by David Grene (Chicago: University of Chicago Press, 1988)

Homer, *The Odyssey*, translated by Robert Fitzgerald (New York: Vintage Books, 1961)

Pausanias, *Guide to Greece*, translated by P. Levy (New York: Penguin, 1984)

Pliny the Elder, *Natural History*, translated by John F. Healy (New York: Penguin, 1991)

Strabo, *The Geography*, translated by H. L. Jones (Cambridge, MA: Harvard University Press, 1982)

The World Wide Web

The *Amazeing Art* website: www.amazeingart.com

Caerdroia, the Journal of Mazes and Labyrinths: www.labyrinthos.net

Andrian Fisher hedge maze design: www.mazemaker.com

The St. Louis Labyrinth Project: www.labyrinthproject.com

The Labyrinth Society: www.labyrinthsociety.org

ACKNOWLEDGMENTS

This book would not have been possible without help that I have received from several people. First and foremost are my family, who supported me in my harebrained scheme to pursue such an unusual project; my agents, Mike Larsen and Elizabeth Pomada, who glimpsed the potential of my work so many months ago and have encouraged me all along the way; and my partner, Patricia, whose patience and support during my forays into the depths of the Berkeley library system were boundless. Special thanks also go to my editors at HarperCollins, Larry Ashmead and Krista Stroever, for their great kindness and many creative contributions. The comments and help I have received from Prof. Jeremy Rutter at Dartmouth College, and from Dr. Sean Hemingway at the Metropolitan Museum of Art, were invaluable. I would also like to thank my research assistant at Berkeley, Laura Steele, whose early work gave me a head start in formulating my ideas for the book, as well as my friend Eve Kushner for her helpful comments on the early drafts of the essays and introduction. A particularly enthusiastic thanks is due to Prof. Carla Goodnoh of Dartmouth College, for without her many contributions, suggestions, criticism, and hard work, this book would not have been what it is.